MW00652670

The Nature of Earth:
An Introduction to Geology
Part III

Professor John J. Renton

THE TEACHING COMPANY ®

PUBLISHED BY:

THE TEACHING COMPANY
4151 Lafayette Center Drive, Suite 100
Chantilly, Virginia 20151-1232
1-800-TEACH-12
Fax—703-378-3819
www.teach12.com

ISBN 1-59803-222-4

John J. Renton, Ph.D.
Professor of Geology, West Virginia University

John Renton received his bachelor's degree in chemistry in 1956 from Waynesburg College, Waynesburg, Pennsylvania. Although he had originally planned to earn a master's degree in chemistry, having had his interest piqued by a course in geology taken in his senior year and encouraged by his professor, he decided to pursue a master's degree in geology, which he received in 1959 from West Virginia University. Commissioned as a second lieutenant in the U.S. Air Force in 1959, Dr. Renton spent his tour of duty as a Research and Development Officer in the Solid-State Physics Group at Wright-Patterson Air Force Base in Dayton, Ohio. Upon completion of his military duty and having decided on a career in university teaching, he returned to West Virginia University, where he was awarded the Ph.D. in 1963. The year Dr. Renton graduated, the Department of Geology decided to expand into the area of geochemistry and offered him a faculty position to do just that. He established and taught courses in aqueous geochemistry, instrumental analysis, x-ray analysis, and clay mineralogy. With government interest rising in coal, he and a colleague established courses in coal geology and coal geochemistry. Throughout his tenure, however, his favorite course has been introductory geology, which he has taught for 40 years.

In his specialty of coal geology and geochemistry, either alone or with co-workers, Dr. Renton has published 45 papers and has been part of more than $4 million of coal-related research grants. His current research interest is the distribution of selenium and arsenic in coal and coal-related rocks and their mobility when exposed to weathering. In addition to his scientific investigations, Dr. Renton and three colleagues have established a program to provide content, workshops, and field experiences for earth science teachers throughout West Virginia.

With few students currently interested in coal, Dr. Renton's teaching responsibilities are primarily focused on two 280-student introductory geology courses each semester. Based on his experiences in teaching introductory students and in recognition of their special academic needs, he has written a textbook, *Planet Earth*, published by Kendall-Hunt. Dr. Renton's success in teaching is indicated by the number of teaching awards he has received. In 1995, he won the Outstanding Educator Award from the Eastern Section of the American Association of Petroleum Geologists. In 2000, he won the Outstanding Teacher Award from the Eberly College of Arts and Sciences, and in 2001, he won the university-wide Outstanding Teacher Award from the West Virginia University Foundation and also West Virginia Professor of the Year from the Carnegie Foundation for the Advancement of Teaching and the Council for the Advancement and Support of Education (CASE Award). His most prestigious award came in 2002, when he was appointed to the Eberly Family Chair for Distinguished Teaching.

Table of Contents
The Nature of Earth: An Introduction to Geology
Part III

Professor Biography i

Course Scope 1

Lecture Twenty-Five   Karst Topography 5

Lecture Twenty-Six   Groundwater Contamination............................ 20

Lecture Twenty-Seven   Rock Deformation.................................... 35

Lecture Twenty-Eight   The Geologic Structures 51

Lecture Twenty-Nine   Faults and Joints.................................. 68

Lecture Thirty   Earthquakes.. 85

Lecture Thirty-One   Damage from Earthquakes............................ 102

Lecture Thirty-Two   Seismology... 119

Lecture Thirty-Three   The Formation of Mountains 136

Lecture Thirty-Four   Orogenic Styles.................................... 152

Lecture Thirty-Five   Economic Geology of Coal........................... 169

Lecture Thirty-Six   Economic Geology of Petroleum...................... 185

Timeline 200

Glossary 202

Biographical Notes.. 227

Bibliography 230

The Nature of Earth: An Introduction to Geology

Scope:

Geology has got to be considered the world's number-one spectator sport. Consider the millions of people worldwide who travel millions of miles to visit and experience monuments that nature has carved out of rock. Each year, tourists stand in awe on the south rim of the Grand Canyon on the edge of a chasm that is more than a mile deep and, in places, more than 10 miles wide. Others stand among the incredible thermal features of Yellowstone Park, one of the truly unique places in all the world. Although visitors can appreciate such places with absolutely no geological knowledge, I cannot help but feel that if they had at least a basic understanding of how these features originated, they would be even more impressed. How much more would a trip to the Grand Canyon mean with the understanding that what lay before you was the result of a huge portion of the southwest that we now call the Colorado Plateau having been lifted vertically from near sea level to elevations of 10,000 feet? The result was a rejuvenated Colorado River and its tributaries that methodically cut through thousands of feet of rock to create the scenic splendor you see from Canyonlands in the east to Zion National Park in the west. Likewise, as you stand in the middle of Yellowstone Park surrounded by hundreds of hot springs, fumaroles, and geysers, the power of nature is obvious. But how much more will that experience mean if you understand that all of what you see within the park is the result of the movement of the North American continent over a hot spot that developed about 16 million years ago beneath what is now northeastern Nevada? Further, that hot spot was responsible for the volcanism that created the Snake River Valley of southern Idaho as the continent moved to the west-southwest, and it eventually ended up under the northwestern corner of Wyoming. Would it not mean more as you observed an eruption of Old Faithful to know that you were standing in the middle of an enormous collapsed structure that formed following three incredible eruptions, the likes of which have never been experienced in all of historic time? Would it not mean more to know that only a few miles beneath your feet, molten rock is rising toward the surface, creating a bulge that explains why Yellowstone Lake is being tipped to the south and that this bulging of the surface may well be a premonition of another cataclysmic eruption? I cannot help but feel that it would.

It is my purpose in preparing this course to give you the basic knowledge you will need to understand much of what you see around you as you tour the world, whether that tour represents going to some distant exotic place or the short trip to the office or shopping center. There will be much to learn beyond what I will teach you here, but what you will gain in this course will be a sound foundation for further investigation on your part. As I will point out in my first lecture, my aim is to have you carry what you learn in this course with you wherever you go for the rest of your life so that you may more deeply understand and appreciate the landscape and the geology that surrounds you.

I have always thought that a course in introductory geology should begin by placing Earth in the context of the Universe. To this end, in Lectures One and Two, we will review some of the ideas astronomers have about the Universe, from its creation with the Big Bang to its possible end. In these early lectures, we will concentrate on the stars, because the elements that are the building blocks of everything are created during the deaths of stars. Having created the elements, we will discuss the origin of planets, using our own solar system as a model. We will then use the discussion describing the formation of planet Earth from its protoplanet predecessor to introduce the topic of plate tectonics.

The theory of plate tectonics revolutionized how we envision Earth. It is to geology what Darwin's concept of organic evolution was to biology, Newton's laws of motion were to physics, and Copernicus's view of the heavens was to astronomy. Because plate tectonics will be the basis for many of our discussions, it is important that you have an understanding of it early in the course. Lectures Three and Four will be devoted to the theory of plate tectonics.

We will then move on to a discussion of the materials of which Earth is made in Lectures Five through Seven, namely, minerals. Minerals are the building blocks of rocks. Because much of what you will see in your travels is either composed of rocks or consists of the remains of rocks that have been exposed to the atmosphere, it is important to have a firm understanding of basic mineralogy and how minerals combine to form the three different kinds of rocks: igneous, sedimentary, and metamorphic. It is also important to understand that the geologic history of Earth is recorded in rocks and that the primary purpose of the science of geology is to determine Earth history. To these ends, we will discuss how minerals form, what determines their relative chemical stability, and how they combine to form rocks.

Because igneous rocks make up the great portion of Earth's surface, in particular the crust, we will introduce in Lecture Eight the process by which many types of igneous rocks form, that is, volcanic activity. We continue our discussion of rock types in Lectures Nine and Ten, where we take a look at the composition and formation of sedimentary and metamorphic rocks. In Lectures Eleven through Thirteen, we will call on plate tectonics to demonstrate how the theory allowed us to finally understand the distribution of volcanic activity, a process that had been observed for many centuries but never fully understood.

Lectures Fourteen through Sixteen will introduce the major processes that constantly change Earth's land surface, including mass wasting and weathering. For the most part, these processes go on at such slow rates that, except for the occasional landslide or flood, few people are aware of their existence, yet their combined efforts are responsible for the sculpting of the topography that surrounds all of us. These discussions will represent a giant step toward your understanding of much of what you see as you tour your world. Lectures Seventeen and Eighteen discuss the topics of soil minerals and soil types. Lectures Nineteen through Twenty-Two take up the topic of erosion, beginning with the main agent of erosion—streams—and how they sculpt the land and ending with a look at the second most important agent of erosion—glaciers.

The topic of groundwater is introduced in Lectures Twenty-Three through Twenty-Six, mainly because it represents our major supply of readily available fresh water; in this country, more than half of our drinking water comes from groundwater sources. In many parts of the country and the world at large, obtaining fresh water is now and will become an increasingly serious problem. Unfortunately, too many people consider groundwater to be a renewable resource; you will discover in these discussions that it is not.

Lectures Twenty-Seven through Twenty-Nine discuss the various processes under which rocks are deformed and the basic geologic structures that are created by the deformational forces. During your travels, except for rocks whose layers are horizontal, the attitudes of rocks you observe in road cuts and the faces of cliffs are the result of rock deformation.

Lectures Thirty through Thirty-Two discuss perhaps the most life-threatening aspect of rock deformation, namely, earthquakes. We will again resurrect our discussions of plate tectonics to explain the worldwide distribution of earthquakes. For centuries, observers noted that the distributions of life-threatening volcanic activity and earthquakes seemed to be directly associated, a relationship that was only understood with the advent of plate tectonics. Using plate tectonics, we will explain what determines the magnitude of earthquakes and what, if anything, can be done to minimize their damage. Included in these lectures will be a discussion of how seismic waves are recorded and studied.

Lectures Thirty-Three and Thirty-Four will concentrate on what many geologists consider the essence of the science, namely the creation of mountains. Once again, we will see that until the advent of the theory of plate tectonics, we never really understood how the great mountains of the world formed. At first thought, it would seem that there should be an infinite number of ways such structures could come about. Plate tectonics shows us that all of the major mountains of the world can be explained using a few plate-dominated scenarios.

We will close the course with two lectures that concentrate on the two major sources of energy in modern society, coal and petroleum, in particular, oil. We are fast approaching a crisis in the availability of the oil that has been the world's major energy source since early in the last century. According to the best estimates, the end of the hydrocarbon era will come before the end of this century. Certainly, our children and grandchildren will face the end of the oil era. At the present time, the only readily available long-term source of energy for the future is coal. But because coal is also a non-renewable resource, we must find one that is not. I would suggest hydrogen.

Lecture Twenty-Five
Karst Topography

Scope:

Karst topography is the result of the slow dissolution of limestone beds forming a network of passageways, usually following joint systems that intersect almost at right angles throughout the rock. As the limestone dissolves, sinkholes form. When the water table drops below the tops of the passageways, caves and caverns are formed. In caves fully above the water table, carbonate-rich groundwater, percolating from above, is responsible for the creation of the beautiful dripstone features for which such caves are famous. Collectively called *speleothems*, these features include stalactites and stalagmites.

Outline

I. Perhaps one of the most spectacular results of groundwater in action is the development of *karst topography*.

   A. Karst topography is a particular lay of the land named after the Karst Valley in Yugoslavia and is usually found in valleys in humid regions.

   1. A characteristic of karst valleys is the absence of through-flowing streams. Any streams are rapidly subsumed underground in *swallow holes*.

   2. Equally characteristic of karst topography are sinkholes, typically arranged in orthogonal patterns.

   B. Underlying the surface is a relatively thick layer (tens to hundreds of feet thick) of pure limestone—that is, 95% calcium carbonate, with the remaining 5% as insoluble residues.

   C. The limestone is characterized by cracks that intersect almost at right angles. There are two sets of cracks: In one set, the cracks align parallel to each other; the other set lines up perpendicular to the first set.

   D. The downward percolation of acidic rainwater dissolves the limestone, in particular at the intersections of cracks (called *joints*). As the limestone is dissolved along the intersection of two joints, it forms cone-shaped holes. The surface becomes depressed, forming a sinkhole. Most sinkholes are solution sinkholes.

E. Karst topography is typically grassy and often used for raising cattle.

II. Passageway development occurs when the limestone layer, at this point an aquitard, is completely below the water table.

A. The water runs through the joints, forming thin passageways that turn at right angles.

B. After millions of years, the diameter of the passageways increases to become tunnels that form octagonal patterns below the water table. During this time, the surface of the land and the regional water table are being lowered relative to the limestone layer, which becomes a super-aquifer. Eventually, the result is caves and caverns. When the water table drops below the tops of the passageways, a zone of aeration develops that may ultimately extend throughout the cave system.

C. As the water table continues to drop, it reaches the cave floor. Surface waters may accumulate there in the form of ponds.

D. With the cave system now completely above the water table, the water percolating through the overlying limestone and heading toward the water table must cross the cave system. Drops of water collect on the cave roof and eventually fall to the cave floor.

    1. With each drop, a tiny deposit of $CaCO_3$, commonly referred to as *dripstone*, forms at the point of drop formation and spatter. As this process continues for additional periods of geologic time, the cave becomes adorned with features collectively called *speleothems*.

    2. Conical structures called stalactites build down from the cave roof.

    3. Other conical structures called stalagmites build from the floor.

    4. Eventually, a stalactite and stalagmite may meet to form a pillar.

    5. In some cases, sheets of dripstone descend along a crack to form what spelunkers call *bacon rind* or *bridal veils*.

E. In regions where the cave system is still below the water table, the rock section above the cave roof is being supported by the groundwater in the cave. During long periods of drought, as the regional water table drops below the roof of the cave, the overlying rocks lose their support and the cave roof collapses to form a collapse sinkhole. An earthquake shock wave, which moves rocks horizontally and vertically, can also cause caves to collapse into sinkholes.

F. A problem with karst topography is the potential for groundwater contamination.

G. In addition to limestone, karst topography can also be produced with gypsum, though this is much less common than limestone.

H. Finally, karst topography features karst towers, which are formed when weathering removes the top of the cave passageways. Examples can be found in southern China.

Recommended Reading:

Price, M, *Introducing Groundwater.*

Questions to Consider:

1. Why do solution sinkholes commonly occur in orthogonal surface patterns?

2. Under what conditions do speleothems form?

Lecture Twenty-Five—Transcript
Karst Topography

If I had to pick one feature that had to be the most impressive feature formed as a result of the activity of groundwater, it would have to be called *karst topography*. The name *karst*, I might add, comes from a valley in Yugoslavia, and it's the lay of the land. That's what *topography* is, and it turns out that karst topography usually is in a valley—although I've seen these features developed on hilltops and ridgelines—but usually it is in the valley.

And if you drive into a typical karst valley, how would you recognize it? Certainly one of the things you would notice would be that there were few—if any—through-flowing streams. For example, a stream might flow into one end of the valley, but as soon as it enters into the karst valley it disappears underground through what they call *swallow holes* in the stream channel. The channel may continue through the valley and almost always does, but it won't have water in it, except if it's actually raining. Then the water will collect only during the rain, and then when the rain stops the water disappears again through these swallow holes underground. And then the interesting thing is down at the other end of the valley it may just come back to the surface again. So I think it gives you some idea that there's something going on underneath the ground that's really— well, we'll get around to talking about what that is, okay.

Now, the other thing that characterizes the valley—and this is probably the most obvious thing as you drive into the valley—there will be these circular to elliptical shape depressions in the ground. We call them *sinkholes*, and they can be any size you want. They can be the size that you can straddle with your legs, or they can be many, many feet across. So there's no size requirement for these things. If you could look at them from the air or on a map, one of the things that you would notice would be that there's an orthogonal arrangement to the pattern of these things. They're not just sort of random—anywhere they want to be. And so one of the first things I would like to describe and explain, number one—where do these sinkholes come from, and why do they have that orthogonal arrangement like that?

Well, to do that, let's picture, for example, what's underneath the ground. Directly underneath the ground in order for karst topography to exist, the absolute requirement is that you have a layer of limestone, relatively thick. Now, we're not talking about maybe six inches or a foot: We are talking about a layer of limestone that may be measured in tens of feet, maybe even hundreds of feet. So we're talking about a thick layer of limestone, and the other characteristic of the limestone: It has to be pretty pure. We're talking a limestone that would be 95% or greater calcium carbonate. The remainder, the other 5%, is what we call *insoluble residues*, and that's just things that really aren't soluble in water. But, anyway, 95%—so it is a pure limestone, relatively thick.

Now picture, if you will, just stripping away from the top of this limestone, for the moment, all of the regolith and all of the soil, so you're looking at the top of the limestone. Well, what you would see is the limestone is broken by cracks. We've talked about these cracks before. These are the same cracks that provided the porosity and permeability that we call *fracture porosity*. And as a result, what these things are—and we'll talk about how they form later—but the interesting thing is if you look at them they intersect each other in almost, not quite, but almost right angles. If you can sort of picture the overall top of this piece of limestone, there are two sets of these cracks. They all line up parallel to each other, and then there's another set perpendicular to that one. So, you have these perpendicular intersections between these cracks.

Think, now, about water moving down through this layer of limestone heading for the groundwater table. Question: Where would be the easiest pathway for that water to move? For example, here's a crack—do you think the easiest pathway would simply be down along any one of those cracks, heading toward the groundwater table below? —Or B, how about where the cracks intersect? I would think that where those things intersect—that would be the more logical place for the water to move down through, where you have these intersections. So now you have a bigger pathway for the water.

Let's picture the water now, moving down through these intersections. The limestone's water-soluble, so as the water moves down—remember now, it's not just water: It's a dilute solution of carbonic acid—it starts to dissolve away the limestone. Of course, the dissolution starts at the top of the limestone and works its way down. So, over time, I think you can sort of picture forming sort of a cone-shaped hole, if you will, aligning itself coaxially with this intersection between these two cracks in the rock. And, of course, depending upon how long the dissolution goes on, it could be of any size you want. Now, with that in mind, let's put the regolith back, and let's put the soil back and whatever, and just like a carpet or a blanket, all of a sudden where you have these holes, the regolith and the soil would simply just sort of fall down into them, or collapse into them, or sink into them. And so, that's why they're called *sinkholes*. These are, as a matter of fact, called *solution sinkholes*, and if you drive through a karst area, these are, without a doubt, the most abundant of all. Most of the sinkholes you see will be solution sinkholes. There's one other one that I want to hold until the end to talk about that's a little more spectacular, perhaps, but not nearly as numerous.

The other thing about the surface—at least in my experience: Wherever you go into these karst valleys, almost invariably they'll be grassy. And the reason why they're grassy—remember: grass likes calcium—is you've got that limestone just beneath the surface, so you've got a lot of calcium for the grass to eat as a nutrient. So these things invariably will be grassy areas and used largely for grazing of animals. I think you can see with all those sinkholes around, it's going to be pretty hard to farm a place like that. I wouldn't want to drive a tractor down into a sinkhole, for sure. So, anyway, they're mostly grassy areas where you're raising cattle, or dairy cattle, or whatever.

Let's talk about something else, though. Let's go down below and look at this limestone. What I want you to picture now is a little cross section, and here you have the surface. Then you have the water table—because I want to put the entire limestone now below the water table. That's very important. The entire limestone now is below the water table. Now, remember: All we're dealing with here is fractures. We talked about fracture porosity and what little bit of permeability gets through those fractures. So, in terms of aquifer, aquiclude, aquitard—this definitely would be an aquitard. It's nowhere near an aquifer, for sure. It's not an aquiclude because you do have water moving through it. But note how the water moves through: It's moving through a crack, and then it runs into a crack and turns at right angles, and then it moves along that crack until it hits another one, and it turns at right angles again. So what's happening is that as the water moves through this layer of limestone, it's making these very tortuous, right-angle turns like that, and that's very important when we get to the final end of our description. Picture now, the water moving through this very tortuous pathway—very little water, very slowly—because this is now an aquitard.

Now, what I usually do in class—and maybe you can picture this better if I did it this way: Picture this limestone layer. And if I put just a thin line through it—just a straight line through it in two dimensions, what that line represents is it's my way of saying that the water is moving through. Not very much water is moving through. And it's moving along a very tortuous, little, thin passageway. But this is limestone. This stuff's water-soluble—so over time what starts to happen is: In that crack where that water's moving through, it starts to dissolve, and it starts to open up. So, now, this little, thin line—I might draw a line right next to it and say, "Okay now, picture that. That's like a little tube moving through there now." As the tube opens up, now, more water can go through. But more water means you're going to dissolve more limestone. This tube that starts off—maybe now it gets bigger in diameter, and now it's sort of like a pipe going through there at right angles, through the limestone. Then we might even picture it getting to the point where it's a tunnel. So, maybe we'll call it a "stop" there. So, picture now, this layer of limestone, and you literally have these tunnels moving through, but note importantly: They move along, turn at right angles, turn at right angles, turn at right angles. Some of them may actually go up into a layer above and go along, or down into a layer below.

So, the idea now is this layer of limestone is just carved out on the inside with these tunnels going in these orthogonal patterns. All of that happened, now, when the limestone was below the water table—and that's the important point to be made. It's all below the water table. Question: How long would that take? I don't know even at the rate that limestone dissolves—pretty slow remember—But, still, something like that would take, I would say, millions of years. So, this is not something that's going to happen overnight. It took millions of years to dissolve all that limestone out. Now we have to what has to be called a *super aquifer*. A million years, a couple of million years, think about what's going on up at the surface now. Up on the surface in the same millions of years or whatever, you've got weathering going on. You've got mass wasting going on. You've got erosion going on. So, the surface now starts to be eroded away, and the surface now starts to come down lower, and lower, and lower, and lower—and as it comes down, the water table now starts to drop. As the water table drops, along with bringing down the surface, eventually the water table may get to the point where it's just below the top of one of these tunnels, just below. Remember, now, everything above the water table is empty of water. So, what we're seeing is that there's going to be a little space at the top of one or more of these tunnels where you're going to have air space up there. It's not going to be very big at the start: It has to start small. But as time goes on, and the surface continues to be worn away, and the water table continues to drop, pretty soon the water table drops down to the point where now this zone of variation or this air pocket at the top gets pretty extensive. It may extend all the way through the cave system.

I think you see what's going to happen here: As time goes on and the water table continues to drop maybe this air space gets so big that now people who crawl into these things can do that and crawl underground. We're talking here about the formation of *cave* and *caverns*, of course. Now, we have the spelunkers. The spelunkers come on the scene. And that's what a *spelunker* is: A *spelunker* is someone who just loves to crawl underground in these caves and caverns. I personally go into caves and caverns when they become commercial—in other words, when they have the sidewalks, and the handrails, and the colored lights. I was coerced, shamed actually, by a bunch of a students one time to go into one of these non-commercial caves. And it is scary. I mean, you haven't experienced dark until you've gone into a cave and somebody turned the lights out. You can feel the darkness. I remember being in there. I said, "Please get me out of here, and I will never, never go back." Well, I did get out of there, and I kept my promise: I've never been back. But anyway, so now, we have a *cave system*. That's how caves and caverns form.

Picture this now: The water table may continue to drop, and eventually it gets down to pretty much the bottom of the cave system, but it's still above the cave bottom in many places. So, what would it look like in there? Remember it's still the same rules down there as up there: So where the water table is above the cave bottom surface, you might have streams in there. You'll have ponds in there. I don't know if it'd get big enough to call it a *lake*, but you have surface waters accumulating. Then note: If the water table then got to the point where it dropped below the bottom of the cave, then the cave goes dry. So, in other words, whether the cave is wet, or dry, or whatever is simply determined by where that water table is. Now, we've got this cave system. Note the important point: The system now, the cave system itself—where it goes, how big the passageways are—all of that was created when the limestone was below the water table, below. Once that water table started dropping down across the cave system, then for all intents and purposes the cave creation, the system, is over. You're not going to get any new passageways. You might get a rock fall in a roof so you have a bigger room now than you had before. But as far as the passageways themselves—where they go, how big they are—that phase now is over. The cave system has been completed.

Now, picture that we have this cave system completely above the water table. The water table is down below the cave system. Then we go into phase two. In phase two what happens? Well, it's still raining up above. The water's still sort of coming down, heading toward the groundwater table, you see, which is below this cave system now. And it comes down through the limestone at the top of the cave, and as it comes through that limestone layer it's still carbonic acid, so it's still dissolving a little bit of calcium carbonate. Then it beads up on the ceiling. And what it wants to do, of course, is get down to the water table. And to do that it has got to cross the cave system. So a bead forms up there, or a drop of water, and then it drops down to the cave floor and spatters, and then a little bit of water that's up there evaporates and deposits a little bit of calcium carbonate up there where the drop had been. And down here where the spatter took place, a little bit of calcium carbonate deposits where the spatter took place. And then another drop forms, and the same thing goes on—so drop by drop by drop, spatter by spatter by spatter, you start to have this structure composed of calcium carbonate; the common name is *dripstone*. And I think you can see why they call it dripstone, because drop by drop by drop is how this stuff forms.

Here you have—coming down from the ceiling—this pendulous structure hanging down from the ceiling, and another one, somewhat stumpier, building up from the cave floor. Now, the name for all of these things—they call them *speleothems*. Now, here are the two most common ones: The one hanging from the ceiling and the one building from the floor—one is called a *stalagmite*, and the other is *stalactite*. Now, I always ask my students which one is which?

Which ones do the hanging, and which ones are building from the floor of the cave? Obviously, you have a 50–50 chance of making this thing right. But here's the way to remember it. I have, lo these many years. *Stalagmites* with the "m" build up from the floor, and *stalactites* with a "t" points down from the ceiling.

So, here you have, then, within this cave system, all these structures starting to form on the cave ceiling and up from the floor. Eventually they'll grow together, and then you have things—they call them *columns,* or *pillars,* or whatever. But the other thing that can happen is that the drops, rather than forming just from a spot up there, maybe they form along a crack. Remember we still have these cracks that we were talking about before. So here's a bunch of drops forming along a crack. And then they're dropping along that crack to the bottom down here, to the floor. And as a result, the calcium carbonate—this dripstone, if you will—doesn't come down as a stalactite, but it sort of comes down as a sheet like that, just moving down through. Well, then they have names for those things too. They call those things a *bacon rind* or *bridal veil.* So they have names for all those things. So, pretty soon the cave system is filled with these absolutely incredible structures, and that's the reason why people go into caves. If you've never been in one, go into one. They are absolutely spectacular, and it's absolutely incredible what Mom Nature does down there in terms of creating things out of dripstone.

Now, again, how long does that phase take? Millions of years, we're talking a long, long time to make those things. Here's a point: I had a student one time who was a big caver, a spelunker. He asked me if I would ask all of my students in the future to please do something, or not do something. He asked me to make this plea, and for all lo these many years I have done this to all my students, and since you're my students I want to ask you to do the same thing. His comment was: When you go into these caves and these cavern systems—now, we're talking, now, about a non-commercial one because if you go into the commercial caves like I would go into you can't get at these things: They have them sort of cordoned off, or you'll have railings, and you can't get up against them—but if you go into a non-commercial cave where you can actually get up front and personal with these things, his comment, for example, was, "Don't just go in and break one off for a souvenir." A lot of people do that. I've seen people coming out of these caves, and they're carrying a piece of stalactite. Or they have these things called *soda straws.* They just look like a soda straw; they're about yay long. Now, these things take, how long? I don't know how long they take, but it's a long, long time, and people will break those off and bring them out. Why? They're just going to get thrown out of your house anyway. It's like walking out in the woods and picking wild flowers. Why would you do that? As soon as you pick a wild flower it's dead. So why not leave it for someone else to see and enjoy, and let it die its own natural death, and for another one to come up, but don't do that. But, anyway, his comment was even more than that. His comment was, "Please don't even touch those things." Because according to him—and I suspect he's right, I see no reason to believe he isn't right—he said that even the oil from your fingers getting on the surface of that dripstone means that in the future anything else that would grow there would not be growing the way it was originally. So by just touching these things, what you're really doing, you're actually deforming anything that would form in the future. His comment was, "Go into the caves, look at the stuff, enjoy it for what it's worth, but just leave it behind and don't touch it." Like I say, I've been asking students for a lot of years to do that, and so I'm carrying on his plea. So, anyway, if you ever get into one, don't touch these things.

There's one other kind of sinkhole I do want to talk about, and this is called a *collapse sinkhole*. Now, these collapse sinkholes—these are the kind of sinkholes that you're going to see if you're dealing with an area that hits the newspapers. You don't read about the formation of solution sinkholes because they're just going on forever. The collapse sinkholes are the ones that appear in the paper and on TV because they can, in fact, be very, very destructive. Here's the picture. Let's picture, again, a cave system, but this time we're going to put it down below the water table again. So, here's a cave system completely filled with water, with a roof over top of it, a stack of rocks over top. The question is: What supports the weight of all the rocks above? The answer to that is: It's the water in the cave. Remember water, now, is incompressible. It's the idea of the weight of the overlying rocks is being supported by this mass of incompressible water, and it would be just like you filled the cave with concrete, it would be the same thing. So it's supporting the roof.

Here's what happens though. Let's say we have a scenario where this particular place, and the place I'm thinking about where you see a lot of this is in Florida. Because if you ever go to Florida, the interesting thing about the Florida peninsula, all it is really is a big development of limestone sticking out there into the ocean. So underneath almost all of Florida, you're dealing with these layers of fairly pure limestone. You get to see a lot of these things. The picture now is this layer of limestone, once completely filled with water. Now, you go into a period of drought. And I'm not talking about a drought that lasts maybe a couple of days or maybe a couple of weeks: I'm talking about a drought that may last for a year or more, years perhaps. So you go into these long periods of drought, where it's almost a change in climate, so to speak. Well, what happens— remember, it's a precipitation thing—as the precipitation drops off what starts to happen is the water table starts to drop again, just like before. As the water table drops, eventually it's going to drop below the roof of the cave, and all of a sudden this cave roof is no longer being supported from below.

Now what's going to happen? It depends upon how strong the rocks are on the roof of the cave. If, for example, the rocks on the roof of the cave are thick enough they can certainly support their own weight and nothing will happen. Maybe it will drop all the way down through in the scenario we just described. You'll start forming these speleothems within this cave. But let's say the thickness of the cave roof rock was nowhere near thick enough to support its own weight. What's going to happen is that as that support from below is removed, the rock above is simply going to collapse into the cave system itself, and you're going to end up with a collapse sinkhole. These things are usually very, very large. Well, they don't have to be, but oftentimes the one they picture and you see in the news are. You can talk about one that may be several hundred feet or more across. I'm thinking of the one that really was probably one of the more infamous, if you will, that formed in Florida. This particular collapse sinkhole actually took away a pretty good part of the town. As I remember, it took away the town swimming pool and a couple of buildings. But one of the buildings it took away—well, almost took away—it took away half of a Porsche garage. Now, the thing I remember most about that picture was this Porsche 911 sitting in the debris pile at the bottom of this sinkhole, half buried in debris, with its nose sticking up in the air. And I saw that thing, and I went, "A 911, I always wanted a 911." And here's this thing. It just sort of really tugged at my heart.

If you go into areas like that you'll find these collapse sinkholes. Now, another time these collapse sinkholes can form is during earthquakes. We're going to talk about earthquakes—I can't remember how many lectures it is until our earthquake discussion. But here's another one, oftentimes, you'll have these cave systems, and, again, you'll have a shock wave go by, an earthquake shock wave. Now, we'll talk a lot more about these shock waves and how destructive they can be. In these shock waves, the rocks are being moved basically in two ways. The rocks are being moved either back or forth like that, horizontally, or then the big one, the other one, the rocks are being moved vertically. Actually what's happening is the rocks are being moved in sort of a cyclic fashion like that. So, picture then: You have this cave system, not too terribly far beneath the ground, and you've got, therefore, roofs over these caves, not too terribly thick. This earthquake shock wave goes through moving the rocks back and forth and up and down, I think you can see, once again, if the thickness of the rocks and the roof of the cave is not thick enough, the caves will collapse and form these collapse sinkholes. So, in these areas that have experienced earthquakes it is very, very common to have lots and lots of these collapse sinkholes form. So, anyway, those collapse sinkholes are sort of the destructive phase of the whole system.

Anyway, karst topography, just one last comment, we're going to talk a little bit about contamination of groundwater. That's one of the real problems you have to face in karst areas unfortunately. Because, you see, you have things like even solution sinkholes, let alone the collapse sinkholes, and these can act as conduits down in to the groundwater table. And anything you do above in the way of, let's say, fertilization or anything that you're doing above in, for example, getting rid of garbage, which we'll talk about—these things can be direct access right down into the groundwater table. So, one of the problems they have in karst areas—and I'm thinking of our own karst area in West Virginia in the southern part of the state—is the potential for groundwater to become contaminated. The problem when groundwater becomes contaminated, it is very, very difficult to decontaminate it. What's going to happen, let's say you have a stream that becomes contaminated. Well, it's simply a question, in that case, of taking the water out of the stream, putting it through some kind of a chemical treatment system—and that's basically what water treatment systems are in municipal water supplies: You're taking the water supply that might not pass the EPA laws, and you're turning it into a water supply that does pass the EPA laws—so that's one thing. But once those things get into the groundwater, it's almost impossible to get rid of them. I will admit that as water moves through aquifer systems, the rocks themselves have an incredible ability, now, to sort of clean up and remove certain pollutants. But there are certain things that it can't. And the problem is downstream this water we're talking about that is draining out of this karst region can actually become into an aquifer that's feeding into somebody's well. So, the whole area of contaminating water supplies becomes increasingly severe and important when you're dealing with these karst areas.

So, anyway, there's you karst topography, and there are lots of places within the United States that have it. And oh, one thing in closing—just for my gypsum friends: It turns out that we were talking about all these things forming where you have limestone. Well, you can also form karst topography if underneath the ground you have a layer of gypsum—remember now, gypsum: calcium sulfate dot waters—and it's also water-soluble. So things like gypsum layers, if they're thick enough and pure enough, and also, of course, salt, if it's close enough to the surface, can form these underground solution cavities. So, limestones aren't the only form of karst topography. But I would say, at least in my experience, all the ones I have ever seen have been the result of this dissolution of limestone. There's one of the most, I think, incredible features that form as a result of groundwater, it's just karst topography. So if you get a chance to go into a cave and see this stuff, pick a commercial one because they're easier to get into and out of.

Something just popped into my mind. There's another feature I'd like to describe for you. Now, I've never seen any of these: They are things called *Karst Towers*. Here's the picture: You're dealing, again, with a karst system where the cave system has already developed. But we're talking—here in the situation I'm thinking of, the place I'm thinking of—a layer of limestone, very, very thick: hundreds of feet thick. So picture, if you will, this thing being carved out with all of its caves, and caverns, and all that stuff. And then what's going to happen, now, is we're going to drop the water table and bring all this stuff *above* the water table and develop, if you will, all the speleothems and all the other stuff we talked about. This stuff, now, is going to be exposed at the surface. In other words, the cave system is down below, but you've got a surface up there. This would be a typical karst surface. Then what's going to happen, well, just good old-fashioned weathering, and mass wasting, and stream erosion, again, is going to start taking away that top. And note: As it keeps wearing its way down, pretty soon that layer that was making the roofs of all these passageways, now that is removed by erosion.

And now, what you have are the places between the passageways—and there are these big mounds of limestone remaining behind. And basically, they're called Karst Towers. I've never seen a place like that, up close and personal that is. But the place that pops into my mind and the reason why I was thinking of this just as I was closing the last discussion, in Guilin, China—in southern China—you have, probably, the world's best example of these things called Karst Towers. So, there are other things other than just what we described that form, as a result, the end product. That would be very definitely an end product because these towers then, what would happen in that particular part of the world, it's very humid, and so you have chemical weathering that's going to be going on at a pretty good clip. And so, over time, what's going to happen is those Karst Towers are just going to slowly but surely be reduced in mass and height, and pretty soon, if nature takes the course long enough, they'll simply be eliminated. So, that's another very, very impressive feature of karst topography. Maybe someday I'll get to Southern China to see it myself. So, anyway, there's another one for you: I didn't want you to go away without at least hearing about those.

Lecture Twenty-Six
Groundwater Contamination

Scope:

Nearly every human activity, from fertilizing our gardens and yards to parking our cars in parking lots, has the potential to contaminate the groundwater supply. Among the products of human existence, however, garbage ranks high among potential contaminants. Poorly designed and built landfills have the potential to cause significant contamination to groundwater. Another common example of groundwater contamination is saltwater encroachment. Solutions include incineration, where permitted by law, and recycling, where the costs are affordable.

Outline

I.   The potential sources of groundwater contamination are legion. Although solid waste from mining and agricultural waste are major problems, we will limit our discussion to two of the most prevalent examples of potential groundwater contamination.

   A. Garbage is a major problem. Every American generates about 4 ½ pounds of garbage every day, of which about 40% is waste from paper products, 18% is yard waste, 8% is plastics, 8% is glass, and 7% is food waste.

   B. Until 1976, garbage was typically disposed of in open-air solution sinkholes, which had significant potential for contamination.

   C. In 1976, laws were enacted to prohibit the construction of such sinkholes and to require sanitary landfills. The potential for contamination decreased, although it has not been entirely eliminated.

   1.   Ideally, the landfill is constructed over an aquiclude, for example, shale. The use of combinations of impervious plastic liners with compacted clay seals isolates the refuse from the surrounding regolith and bedrock. Further, the garbage is compacted to reduce porosity and permeability in the material itself.

   2.   Perforated piping allows for the detection of effluence, which can be collected and treated for safe disposal. In larger landfills, the gases generated within the decomposing materials can also be collected and used as a fuel to generate electricity.

3. When the landfill reaches capacity, it is again covered with plastic, and vegetation is planted on top. The land can be reclaimed for use as a park or golf course.

4. Problems arise when landfills are filled to capacity and state or municipal law prohibits the creation of a new landfill. Garbage then has to be trucked to another state willing to take it (for a price).

5. One solution to the landfill problem is to use the material as a source of energy by incineration. According to estimates, if we were to burn the material we now place in landfills (called *biomass*), we could generate approximately 10–15% of the energy budget of this country. Of course, the toxins generated from incineration must be removed, but technology exists to accomplish this. A problem with incineration is that some states prohibit the process.

6. Recycling is another possible solution, except that it is expensive; some towns have stopped recycling garbage for that reason.

II. Another common example of groundwater contamination can be found in coastal regions, where groundwater may provide 100% of the fresh water.

A. At the point where the fresh water returns to the ocean, the lower density of the fresh water causes it to ride out over the encroaching saltwater, thereby keeping the saltwater at bay.

B. Increased use of groundwater in coastal regions results in a rise in the saltwater/fresh water interface, a process known as *saltwater encroachment.*

C. Eventually, the saltwater/fresh water interface rises into the bottoms of wells and the wells must be abandoned.

D. In some areas, attempts have been made to depress the saltwater/fresh water interface by constructing large ponds to divert rainwater underground.

III. Another feature associated with groundwater is geothermal activity. Throughout the world are countless places where water is heated either by the geothermal gradient or by underlying magmas that come to the surface.

A. The *geothermal gradient* refers to the temperature increase with depth within the crust of about $25°$ C to $30°$ C per mile of depth. In many areas, hot springs are created by the geothermal gradient as groundwater percolates downward along fractures, perhaps faults; becomes heated; and returns to the surface.

B. In other regions there exist hydrothermal features created when groundwater is heated by near-surface magma bodies. These are rare, existing only in Yellowstone Park, in the northwestern corner of Wyoming; Iceland; and the northern island of New Zealand. The hot water created by the magma rises to the surface, and as pressure is released, the water spouts to the surface in the form of a geyser.

Recommended Reading:

Barcelona, M., *Contamination of Groundwater, Prevention, Assessment, Restoration.*

www.groundwater.org

Questions to Consider:

1. What kinds of materials constitute the great volume of garbage we now bury in landfills?

2. How does one explain the presence of hot springs in regions that do not have underlying sources of magma?

Lecture Twenty-Six—Transcript
Groundwater Contamination

Now in this last lecture of our discussion of groundwater, I'd really like to go back and pick up a little bit more on the contamination of groundwater scene. It's so important to us, and for what reason? Fifty percent of my drinking water and your drinking water comes from it, you see. So I think anything that we should emphasize to people is to understand what the potential problems are.

Well, if you go and look at the potential problems of groundwater contamination, the big one, the big source, of contamination is just the disposal of solid waste. When you think of disposal of solid waste, most of that waste in this country comes from two sources: either mining or from agriculture. Now in the case of mining, what you're usually dealing with is the disposal of material that you had to remove in order to get at whatever you were mining—for example, whether it's coal or iron ore, it makes no difference. Oftentimes—I'm thinking of coal, now, since I know more about it than anything, since that's my specialty area—if you look at the rocks associated with coal, there are minerals in the rocks that could indeed react chemically with the atmosphere (in the case of pyrite) and generate, let's say, pretty strong acids, which potentially could get into the groundwater—if the material was poorly disposed of—and affect somebody's well. So, that would be it. But as far as solid waste from mining, I don't want to really concentrate on that because that's not an immediate problem for us, for most of us. The other one, of course—agriculture—is probably another really, really big one. And I'm thinking of those feedlots you see out in the Midwest—I mean, where you've got thousands and thousands of animals being fattened up for market. And I don't think I need to go in to describe the potential problems of contamination with those.

No, of the two areas I want to talk about, one is a problem that really all of us are involved in or contributing to, and the other one, as we'll see when we get to it, is probably a little bit more localized, but still a pretty big problem for a lot of people.

The one that affects all of us, I think, of course, is garbage. We are the biggest generators of garbage in the world. We generate, in this country, more garbage than any other country in the world. For example, I looked up some numbers, and it turns out the estimate is that every person in this country generates about 4.5 pounds of garbage a day. When you multiply that times the number of people we have in the country, all of a sudden you're dealing with a lot of garbage. Now, to just get an idea of what it is we're having to get rid of: If you look at garbage—and apparently there are people who study garbage, I can't quite imagine doing that as a profession, but anyway—if you look at garbage—the stuff that comes out of your house and my house—most of it is simply paper or paper products. Cardboard, newspapers, magazines—that whole realm of things: That probably, I think, is something like almost 40% of all the garbage we give out of our houses or discharge from our houses. The second one—this really surprised me when I saw this—18% is supposedly yard waste. We're talking grass clippings. I think whoever did that one didn't realize that there were things called *mulching mowers* that we're supposed to use. But anyway, grass clippings, clippings off of trimming or trees or bushes, and of course, at the end of the growing season, all the stuff that's left of the plants in our gardens: all that stuff. So that's about 18%.

And then the next in line are plastics and glass—they're about 8% apiece. Then 7% is food waste: A lot of people just throw their food waste out with their garbage. There are a lot of people who don't, in other words, a lot of people put it in the compost piles—these are real gardeners, of course, who do that. And then the rest is just various kinds of things. The whole point is: These are the things that we simply throw away.

Question: What do we do with them? Up until 1976, what we did with them was we just threw them in a garbage pile. Out there someplace was a place where everybody took their garbage and piled it up. Now, these are *garbage dumps*. They had actually no control over these things. There was no kind of treatment of the materials: The garbage was just thrown there. You can just picture this thing now. I mean, these would be breeding grounds for vermin of all kinds and mosquitoes, and flies that spread disease, and they just really smelled bad. And that was the case up until about 1976.

For example, I remember working in the southern part of the state in the early '70s, and I was actually down in that area we just talked about—the karst area of southern West Virginia. I was doing some chemical studies on streams at the time, and so I was wandering through the area and collecting samples, and I ran up on this sinkhole, now, that was just filled with garbage. And then as I worked along the trend, there was another one filled with garbage, and then another one that was partially filled. These were solution sinkholes. Here we have rain falling on this garbage and, of course, it's a dilute solution of carbonic acid, you see, so we have this acid leaching of this debris. God only knows what was in there. And remember now, that's just a direct access right to the groundwater table. So, I went and complained or commented about that to some of the local officials of the little town that was there. And I was told, "Well, you know, there's no law against it," and there wasn't. That was the problem. Up until 1976 there was no law against having those kinds of garbage dumps. But in 1976, the government passed something called the *Resource Conservation Recovery Act*. I don't know if it ever conserved or recovered anything, but one of the requirements of this act was it prevented any more of the uncontrolled garbage dumps and introduced a whole new era of so-called *sanitary landfills*.

So, that's what I'd like to give a little talk about. I don't want to get into it too far, but I think everybody ought to have some feeling for how these things work, and I don't think very many people do. Why? I don't know of the average person wanting to go and visit a sanitary landfill. But let me tell you what they are and how they work because if it's properly designed and properly built, these are not bad places. You can store things away in the ground and not worry too much—there's always the worry, of course, but not too much—about the potential contamination of the groundwater. So here's what they do. The first thing you do, of course, is find a place that is far removed from the general population as you can get. It's the old "NIMBY" Syndrome: "Yeah, let's bury this stuff, but "Not In My Back Yard" kind of thing. You have to get away from the general population and so, obviously, you're out someplace in the country. But the problem is: There are people living out there, too. They just said, "Well, I'm sorry about that this is where we're going to put the garbage dump, the sanitary landfill." So the first thing they do is they dig a pit. Now, ideally what they want is the bottom of this pit to rest on a really, really good aquaclude—in other words, a really good layer of shale. In other words, the idea is to put something between this deposit we're going to put in here and the groundwater table to protect it. So, if they can find a place like that, that's what they do.

And then what they do is they line this pit with very heavy gauge plastic—chemically resistant plastic. The heavy gauge they do that because when they're compacting all this stuff down as they're filling it, there's always a possibility of puncturing through this stuff. Well, the thicker the gauge is, of course, the less of a possibility that is. Then now, the chemical business: You've got to remember that who knows what's in the garbage they're going to be throwing in there. You're going to have all kinds of chemicals: You can have oxidizers like Clorox™ and bleaches, or you can have solvents of every kind you can imagine. You can have acids. So they have to protect themselves from that. So this liner, now, is basically chemically resistant—or as best they can get it chemically resistant. Then the next thing they do is they lay on top of that a layer of clay-rich sediment. This is just like a soil kind of thing. They pack it down, and they form what they call a *clay seal.* Now, once they compact it down, the porosity and permeability of this clay seal, now, is very, very, very low. So now we have another sort-of an artificial aquiclude. While they're doing all that, what they do is they install perforated piping within the base of this thing, the purpose of which is to allow two things to happen. First of all, it allows access to the bottom of this thing to test for any effluence that might accumulate. And the other thing, of course, is if they find it, hopefully they can withdraw it, and treat it, and dispose of it properly. Then on top of the clay seal, they put another layer of plastic, and so now we have two plastic layers and a clay seal—so we have sort-of a triple aquiclude down there.

Then what they do is just start piling in the garbage. Now, if you've ever been to one of these places, what they do to compact it—the machinery is huge. I mean, picture the biggest bulldozer you ever saw with the biggest treads you ever saw in your life. Then they have these other machines—they call them sheepsfoot rollers—they have just like a steamroller, except they have these great, huge prongs sticking out of the wheels that just compact the stuff. The idea is to compact it as much as you can to reduce the porosity and permeability within the material itself. Then the idea is—the way that it's supposed to work—at the end of each day then they will cover that day's garbage with another clay seal. Then they keep doing that until—finally—the whole thing is filled. While they're doing that, oftentimes and most of the time they put standing pipes—again, perforated along the way—to vent the methane gas.

Remember now, this is anoxic reactions down here. During these anoxic reactions you're actually generating methane, CH_4, and you've got to get rid of it: You don't want it to collect down there. So they remove it by these standing tubes. Now, if you were dealing with a relatively small system, then what they do is they just vent it to the air. If you're dealing with a fairly large system, what they'll do is they'll actually collect it and pipe it to some facility close by where they burn it to make heat, to generate steam, to drive a turbine, to make electricity. So, they actually are using one of the byproducts of the system to actually sort of make some money back and cover some of the cost.

So, then when they're finally done, they cover all of that with a plastic layer. Now, this is very important. The problem with all these landfills, the thing you really worry about, is the leaching of that material. You want to keep that dilute solution of carbonic acid—rainwater—away from this stuff. So they cover the whole thing, now, with plastic, and that's supposed to seal everything off. And then on top of that they put down soil and vegetation, and that's the end of it. Then what do they use the land for? It can be used for things like maybe a playground. It could be used for a park. One of the big things I've seen it used for are golf courses. So, things like that. Probably you would not want to put a housing development on top of that, but there are all kinds of other things you can put there. So note that the land is usable once again. I guess that's the whole point.

But here's the problem with these sanitary landfills: They become filled. That's what landfills do—they become filled. And then what do you do? Well, then what you do is move over, and dig another pit, and make another one of those. That's okay if your state or municipality allows that to happen. But the problem is today there are states and municipalities in which by law, you are not allowed to open any new landfills: Once the landfills that are operating today close down, you can't open any more. Just to give you some idea, I looked up some numbers again, and it turns out—let's see, the law for sanitary landfills—1976 was it? From 1978 until 1991, the number of operating landfills in the country dropped from something like 70,000 to 6,000. They're closing down. They're not opening. Why? Because the law says you can't. So, what do they do with their garbage? These states that say you can't open any more sanitary landfills—and I think one of them is New Jersey, I think it is—they send their garbage to other states that will take it and bury it in their state—at a cost, of course. And what really surprises me is to see the distance some of this garbage is hauled for burial. I mean, it seems to me I read, for example, there was garbage that was sent out from New Jersey as far away as New Mexico. Now, that's a long way to take your garbage for burial. Remember that barge that went up and down the East Coast looking for somebody to take it? We're talking about getting rid of this stuff. It's going to be a very serious problem as more and more of these facilities shut down.

What's the answer? Well, let me just suggest a possible answer: burn it. I mean if you look at that garbage list of things we described, once you take out, let's say, the glass and the cans almost everything in that garbage pile that we're throwing away burns. We call that *biomass*, you see. So rather than burying it and worrying about all that stuff leaching out of it and contaminating the groundwater, why don't we just burn it? And there are lots of big cities that do. They have these incinerators, and they burn the material. And they take the heat, and they make steam, and they drive turbines to make electricity, perhaps. Or they'll take the steam and send it to their downtown buildings in order to heat them in the wintertime, and things like that. We're using it. Now, what's the advantage of it? One of the big advantages, of course, is you take this huge mass of garbage, and you reduce it down to an ash. Now, the problem is that sometimes this ash has in it toxic materials that you don't want to get into the environment either. So the ash has to be constantly looked at—and it is. And if it happens to contain some kind of a toxic material, there are ways to remove a lot of that stuff. Then you dispose of the ash in a landfill—but note: It doesn't have to be anywhere near as big this time. And if it does contain toxic stuff that can't be removed, then it's specially handled. But there are ways of getting rid of that.

The other thing people worry about, of course, is the fact that you can put up the stack some kind of volatile metals—like mercury, for example—and you don't want that going into the atmosphere. But the thing is, the engineers are good. They can design these systems to entrap all that stuff. So it seems to me that the incineration should be a serious consideration for this thing. The problem, again, is everybody will say, "Yeah, that's a good idea. Let's just burn that stuff and get rid of it. But not in my backyard." See that "NIMBY" syndrome keeps popping up all the time. But here's the deal: I read an article one time on biomass, and this particular author was trying to impress on the reader just how much energy we could generate if we burned what we're now throwing away. He estimated that we could probably generate somewhere between 10% and 15% of the total energy picture of this country. I don't know if he's right or not, but if he is, let's say 15%. At the moment, coal's only doing 20%. So, the idea is that we're talking about a potential energy source that could indeed provide us some relief, you see, from our energy problems. So, I really think we ought to start thinking about that kind of thing. So, that's one problem. That affects all of us. I think all of us have to consider that whole problem of garbage.

Now, one of the suggestions to take care of the problem has been recycling. You know there seems to be a double-edged sword to that recycling. It's good—don't get me wrong. For example in Morgantown, we recycle paper, glass—both clear glass and colored glass—cans, of course, and *white plastic* they call it. So, we take all that stuff out, and then this recycling takes care of all that. But in a lot of places what they're finding out is the recycling is very, very expensive. They're finding out that it would be cheaper to bury the stuff, in just terms of dollars, than it is to recycle. So should we recycle? Yeah, I still think we should recycle. We've got to keep those things out of those landfills and besides, you know, anything we can do to reduce the cost of all of this, I think we ought to look at. So, anyway, recycling—although there are towns that have dropped recycling just for that very reason. So, anyway, that's a possibility. That, I think, is something that really affects all of us, and so I think all of us ought to think about that in terms of the amount of garbage we generate and throw out there. There are other things we could be doing. We could be doing, for example, taking food waste and put it in a compost pile and putting that back in your garden. You see, we could do that.

The next one I want to talk about, now, this is a sort of local kind of thing. It doesn't really affect everybody, for sure, but it affects the people along the coastline. We're talking now, a very large population. I read one time what percentage of the total population lives within 50 miles of either the Atlantic Coast, the Pacific Coast, or the shorelines of the Great Lakes, and I forgot, I'm sorry. But it's a large number of people. One of the problems they face on coastlines is saltwater encroachment. Okay, so here's the picture I want you to have: Picture a sort-of a slice down through the edge of the coast as it approaches the sea. Here comes the land down to the sea, and it meets the water—that's the shoreline, okay. Now, underneath you have the groundwater table, and this is the regional table, now. Here comes the water table, and it reaches right down to that shoreline. That's where it comes to the surface, you see, it's been underground all the while—except for streams, and ponds, and things like that, I understand that. But it comes back to the surface, finally, right at the shoreline. As a matter of fact, the next time you go to the shore and the tide goes out, just walk along the shore, and sometimes you can see water seeping out of the sand—basically, that's what that is: That's the edge of the water table.

So, here you have the water table. Below the water table, of course, you have this wedge, if you will, of fresh water. Okay, that's what we're going to use—that's our groundwater—but below that what you have is another wedge of saltwater, which is driving underneath the fresh water. You see, the fresh water being lower density will be on top. But there's the problem: It's that saltwater/fresh water interface. So picture, now, an area of the coast—and you get over there, and there are places where 100% of all their water is gotten from wells. So here's a well now, drilled down through the water table into this wedge of fresh water. As long as the population isn't too terribly high, and as long as you're not over-demanding water—over-producing—that saltwater/fresh water interface stays down there, and so it's nowhere near your well. Fair enough. But here's the problem: All you need to do is go to the East Shore.

For example, we took some students down to the Outer Banks—the Barrier Islands, we call them—and I was absolutely aghast. I hadn't been there for quite a while, and the number of condo, after condo, after condo built on there. Now, where did they get all that water? Well, they can't get it from wells anymore because here's what has happened. What has happened is you produce water from that fresh water wedge. All of a sudden that saltwater interface starts to rise, and sooner or later it rises to the point where it intersects the bottom of your well. Once it does that, the game is over. Your well, now, is going to produce saltwater. It's over. Where are you going to get your water? A lot of the water they use down at the shoreline now comes all the way from the mainland, piped out there. Well, that's kind of a pretty expensive way to get water, but that's what they have to do.

Is there anything other than that that you can do? Well, it depends. Let me just describe something. I thought this was actually pretty ingenious when I saw this. The problem is: You're producing too much water from that little freshwater wedge. The saltwater interface has risen. Note: If you could do something to get the water back down below the water table, you could, in fact, push that saltwater interface down to the point where now it's below your well, and you're back in business. How could you do it? Well, it seems to me I saw this—I think I was on Long Island, but I can't be absolutely sure—but here's what they were doing. Picture now, a rain: a really heavy rainstorm or whatever. In order to keep their little area—the little town area—from flooding, what they did was they collected the rainwater into storm sewers and shunted it out into the ocean. That's what they've been doing for years. But then somebody said, "Well, you know, why are you wasting that fresh water? Rather than shunting it out to the ocean, let's get it back down into the aquifer system."

Well, how are you going to do that? Here's the way they did it, and I thought this was kind of ingenious. They dug a pit. This pit was an area about the size of a baseball field—as a matter of fact, during the times when there wasn't water in it, which we'll talk about in a second—it was a baseball field. They had a baseball field in there, and the kids played in there, and the whole bit. In depth this thing was about maybe—I don't know—10 feet deep. Now, here's the deal. During these rainstorms, rather than collecting the water and shunting it out to the ocean, they collected the water and directed it into these pits. And the pits filled up with water during the rainstorm and maybe brim-full or whatever. Now, here you have a pretty good mass of water. Picture now, a mass of water the size of a baseball field 10 feet deep. That's a lot of water. Then the rain stops. What happens? The water just soaks into the ground, back down to the water table again, down below the water table, pushes that saltwater interface below (down further), and all of a sudden now, you have fresh water again.

Does it work? Well, I asked some people in the area, and apparently it did. So, anyway, that was their solution. And I think that was a wake-up call for these people: "You'd better watch how much water you're demanding out of that little freshwater wedge: If you overdo it, that saltwater encroachment's going to come back again." So, I think people living in environments like that have to know. And I think there's the problem right from the start. I think a lot of people, in general, we have in the past—we've done things out there in nature without knowing what the consequences are going to be. I mean if we knew, for example, that over-production from any aquifer is going to eliminate it from use, I think we would have been more conservative with our water demands, you see. But we weren't. We didn't understand how aquifers work. We know now. We better start using our knowledge to preserve our water supplies.

Just to sort of end this particular discussion of groundwater on a sweeter note, I want to pick up a couple of other features of groundwater, that we've actually talked about before, but I want to make another point. These are the hydrothermal features. We're talking hydrothermal features: hot springs, fumaroles, and geysers. Now, we've talked about them before—for example, in terms of volcanic areas. Let's say, hot springs. You can go to any volcanic area and find lots of hot springs. For example, you can go to the Riftalley down in New Mexico, and they're all over the place. You can go to the Great Rift Valley of Africa, and find they're all over the place. Go to Yellowstone Park, and they're everywhere in Yellowstone Park. Now, those waters, now—those hot springs—are the result of the water being heated from magmas down below, so it's a volcanic thing.

The reason that I bring all this up is because somebody asked me about the thermal springs in the East. We have in the Appalachians, strings of thermal events along the Appalachian trend. These are not really hot water, but they are thermally heated. We're talking Warm Springs, Virginia, and Hot Springs, Virginia, for example. Was that heated by magmas down below? No, we don't have any magmas below us any more. There haven't been any magmas below us for hundreds of millions of years. So, now, what heated the water? There's a thing called a *geothermal gradient*, and what the geothermal gradient says is that the deeper you go in the Earth, the deeper you go, things warm up. It averages about maybe 1°C for every 100 feet you go down. I think that's pretty much the rate at which it does. So the idea is: There are places along the Appalachian trend where groundwater, now, is diverted underground along passageways probably on fault zones that are very, very porous—so down it goes to—who knows how far down? But it goes down until it gets hot enough that it starts rising back toward the surface again.

Now, I don't know how hot the water was down there. But by the time it gets back to the surface, these thermal springs aren't really hot. For example, Hot Springs, Virginia—I've been there many times—and it's just sort of, I think, a little bit higher than body temperature. But the point is, they are thermal springs, nonetheless, but they are not heated by magmas; they are not heated by a volcanic source of heat. It's simply the geothermal gradient. So when you talk about hot springs, there are hot springs and then there are hot springs.

The other one I want to comment on, though, are the geysers. I want to comment on them because these are indeed rare features. There are only three places in the world—a little bit of trivia. I love trivia— three places in the world you find geysers: number one, of course, Yellowstone Park—Old Faithful and a bunch of others; Iceland has them; and the Northern Island of New Zealand has them. And that's it. What are they? How do they work? Everybody's seen pictures of the eruption of Old Faithful. What a geyser really is—this is the way I look at it, anyway—it's a combination, sort of a cross between a hot spring and a fumarole. For example, picture, let's say, we take Old Faithful, and she's just erupted. At that moment what's happened is the conduit—which goes deep, deep into the Earth—has just been blown empty of all the water and everything so it's now empty. What happens, then, is groundwater starts to flow into the conduit and heads down toward the bottom. As it heads toward the bottom, of course, it's getting closer and closer to that magma down there, and it starts to heat up—and it gets hotter, and hotter, and hotter. And it reaches the boiling point of water, but it doesn't boil. Why? Because of the pressure of the stack of water above it, so we're talking sort of a pressure cooker scenario here. So, the water keeps getting hotter and hotter down there, but it won't boil because this column of water keeps growing toward the surface. Finally, the water does get to the surface. Now, it's very, very hot—so if you went to the site of Old Faithful, the first thing you would see, finally the water would come to the surface, and it would be steamy hot because it is hot water. Now, all the while now, down at the bottom, that water is continuing to be heated, and eventually it does boil, and it does generate steam. Once the steam forms, it starts forcing that column of water up the hole, and all of a sudden that hot water starts to spout up and pour out of the vent.

Then it just goes like dominos. As it pours out, pressure's relieved down there, more steam is generated down there, and it pushes more water up there. The water starts to spout up in the air and spew all over the place, and then, finally, that steam crashes through, and then you've got this crashing, this big spout, and everybody's taking pictures and doing all. Then it settles down and goes through another cycle. So you see what a geyser is: It's really just a cyclic reaction of a combination of a hot spring and a fumarole. But there are only three places in the world to see them. And the place you do want to go, and please do go someday, is Yellowstone Park. When you get there, just remember down below your feet there's a magma chamber rising. And I'll just let it close there.

Lecture Twenty-Seven
Rock Deformation

Scope:

Once the strength of any solid material is exceeded, it will respond by changing size and/or shape in a process called *deformation*. The first type of deformation is always *elastic deformation*, which is not permanent; the object will bounce back like a rubber band or a tennis ball, leaving no indication that deformation ever occurred. If the elastic qualities of a material are exceeded, it will then deform permanently by *plastic deformation* or *brittle deformation*. *Folds, faults,* and *joints* are the three basic geologic structures. They are produced by *stress*, which involves compression or tension, and *strain*, which can be elastic, plastic, or brittle. The strength of the rock is the third factor driving the process of deformation.

Outline

I. Geologic structures are the result of the interplay among stress, strain, and strength.

   A. Deformation creates mountains. It can be defined as any process in which rock changes in size and/or shape.

   B. Deformation is of three kinds: *faults, folds,* and *joints.*

   C. *Stress* is any applied force; *strain* is a response to stress.

   D. Before any material can undergo strain in response to stress, its strength must be exceeded. *Strength* is the ability to withstand stress without strain. Every material has an inherent strength that must be exceeded by an applied force before anything will happen. Once the stress has exceeded the strength, the material will undergo strain or deformation.

II. Stress is of two basic types: *tension* (pull) and *compression* (push).

   A. In tension, the forces operate in opposite directions and directly away from each other. Examples of tension include pulling a drawer open or stretching taffy.

   B. In compression, the forces act toward each other in two different arrangements.

1. In *non-rotational compression*, the forces act *toward* and *directly opposite* to each other. The hitting of a nail with a hammer or holding a pen are examples of non-rotational compression.

2. In *rotational compression*, the forces act *toward* each other but *not directly opposite*. Because whatever is being acted upon tries to rotate, we refer to this type of compression as rotational compression. Examples of rotational compression would be twisting the cap off a bottle, turning a doorknob, or spreading butter on bread.

III. There are three types of strain: *elastic*, *plastic*, and *brittle*. Strain, or deformation, is always accompanied by a change in size, shape, or both.

    A. In all cases, once the strength of a material is exceeded, the first response will *always* be elastic.

        1. In elastic strain, the applied energy is absorbed and *stored* as the material undergoes deformation.

        2. As long as the force continues to be applied, the energy will continue to be absorbed and stored.

        3. Once the applied force is released, the material will return to its original size or shape, and the stored energy will be *released* in useable form.

        4. The importance of elastic strain is the ability of the material to store and release energy.

        5. Examples of an elastic response include the stretching and release of a rubber band. After it is released, the rubber band returns to its original size and shape, with no indication that anything has happened. Another example is the momentary impact of a tennis ball on a tennis racket. Both the ball and the strings on the racket deform, momentarily absorbing and storing the energy applied by the tennis player, then returning to their original shapes and sizes as energy is released when the ball is driven back.

        6. Every material has an *elastic limit* that restricts the amount of energy that can be stored during elastic deformation. Only after the elastic limit has been exceeded can a material respond by plastic or brittle strain.

B. In plastic deformation, once the elastic limit is exceeded, all the stored energy plus any energy applied subsequent to the exceeding of the elastic limit will be internally *consumed* as deformation takes place.

  1. Plastic deformation is permanent.

  2. An example of a material that undergoes plastic deformation is modeling clay.

C. Materials that undergo brittle strain after the elastic limit has been exceeded will break.

  1. Think of the ringing of a bell, which is an elastic response. The energy of the clapper hitting the side of the bell is released in the form of a sound wave that our ears interpret as a tone.

  2. In the same way, a plate may be thought of as a flat bell. If it is dropped but doesn't break, it makes a sound similar to a bell tone.

  3. On the other hand, if the plate is dropped with more force, it may break into three or four pieces, each of which gives off its own tone. The melding of the tones is the sound of breaking glass.

  4. The plate, or any material, breaks in order to provide additional surface area from which to release the stored energy; the number of breaks depends on the amount of energy that must be released.

  5. Again, if the plate is dropped without much force, it may only crack to provide the extra surface needed to release energy. But if more force is applied—if the plate is thrown at a wall, for example—it shatters to provide the surface area needed to release the greater amount of energy.

  6. Obviously, brittle deformation is also permanent.

IV. The elastic, plastic, or brittle response of rocks to stress is manifest in the geologic structures of *folds, joints,* and *faults.*

  A. Rock folds are an example of a plastic response, a permanent deformation.

  B. Rock faults and joints are examples of a brittle response.

  1. A fault forms where there has been movement and a good deal of energy was released.

2. A joint forms where there has been no appreciable movement and less energy was released.

C. Can a rock have an elastic response? Yes, evidence exists for this phenomenon in Canada.

> **1.** Two million years ago, a thick sheet of ice covered Canada and part of the northern United States. The continental lithosphere was bowed down under the weight of the ice as the asthenosphere flowed out from beneath the region. When the ice finally melted back to the current location of Greenland, water entered the depression to form Hudson Bay.

> **2.** Today, the lithosphere under Hudson Bay is slowly rising, indicating that the lithosphere is returning to its original position, as with an elastic response. If this continues, ultimately, there will be no indication that the deformation ever took place.

Recommended Reading:

Twiss, R. J., and E. M. Moores, *Structural Geology*.

Davis, G. H., and S. J. Reynolds, *Structural Geology of Rocks and Regions*.

Questions to Consider:

1. How is the elastic limit of a material related to the three types of strain that may result from the application of stress?

2. Assume a material has been stressed beyond its strength and begins to undergo strain. What will be the order in which the three types of strain will occur, from first to last?

Lecture Twenty-Seven—Transcript
Rock Deformation

As a geologist, I would consider rock deformation to be just the epitome of geology because the things we're going to talk about, folds and faults, this is what creates mountains—and mountains is where it's at. There's an old saying that says, "The best geologist is the one who's seen the most rocks." Well, if you want to see rocks you go to the mountains because you see them in cliff faces, you see them in road cuts—so that's the place where you're really going to see these things.

So, anyway, rock deformation: *Deformation* simply is any process whereby something changes in size and/or shape. That sort of sets the scene for deformation. Now, the kinds of structures we're going to form, and that's what forms as a result of deformation—the so-called *geologic structures.* They are very, very simple, and there are only three: *faults, folds,* and *joints.* I think to get into this thing, to understand exactly what's going on, we have to start talking a little bit more about these stresses and how rocks and materials in general respond. This is going to be now, my 3-S and 3-B lectures. The 3-S lecture is stress, strain, and strength. And the 3-B lecture is going to be bounce, bend, and break.

Let's take up the 3-S's first. In the little presentation, I have stress off to the left. I have strain off to the right. And in the middle, between the two, I have strength written as though it was some kind of wall. You'll see there's a method to my madness here. Let's just very briefly explain or define what stress is. Very simple: *Stress* is any applied force. Any applied force whatsoever is a stress. A *force* is simply directed energy, so any applied force at all. *Strain*, on the other hand, is a response to stress. In other words, if you apply a force to something, and something happens, then whatever happened, that's the strain. That's all stress and strain is. Now, note: The *strength* written between them sort of like a wall? I meant it that way because the idea is if you apply a stress to something, before anything can happen, you've got to exceed the inherent strength of the material. Everything has an inherent strength. And if you can't exceed the strength of the stuff, then nothing will happen: You'll get no strain.

For example, if you took a 1-inch bar of steel and tried to bend it, I don't think so. Why? It's too strong. On the other hand, if you took just a little piece of copper wire—same force now, same stress—it bends. Why? Well, it wasn't very strong. So, it's a very simplistic idea, I guess, but I think it's a very important one that before you can actually make something happen, there's an inherent strength you've got to overcome.

Let's talk a little bit more detail now about what stress is. Actually, there are only two kinds: *pull* and *push*—that's the bottom line. Pull, of course, the more scientific description of that is tension. Tensional forces are forces that are acting away from each other, so that would be pull. Push, that's where there are forces acting toward each other. If you think about it, I have two different kinds of push. For example, I describe *non-rotational compression*, that's when the forces act directly opposite each other like that. For example, you hold a pencil in your hand if you're writing a letter. That's non-rotational compression. The force between me and this floor is non-rotational compression. The force between that coffee cup and the table—that's non-rotational compression. That's when the forces are acting directly opposite each other.

The other one is rotational compression. In *rotational compression* the forces act toward each other, but not directly opposite. So, the idea is whatever is caught in between tries to rotate, whether it does or not is immaterial. It tries to rotate, so we call that rotational compression. Just think of all the things you've done since you've gotten up this morning. You didn't even have to get up—as you're lying in bed you're always exerting some kind of stress. That would be *non-rotational compression*, you see, as you lie there in bed. But just think of all the things you've done since you got up: You pull a drawer open to get a shirt or a pair of socks: Well, basically, that's tension. You pull the socks on: That's tension, too. You put peanut butter on a piece of bread: That's rotational compression because the peanut butter goes one way, and the knife and the bread goes the other way. It's a relative thing, you see. So, just think of all the things you've done since you got up this morning. They are simply examples of the three different kinds of stress: tension, rotational compression, and non-rotational compression. So, that's all there are.

Now let's talk about strain—what kinds of strains there are. When you think about strain now, there are three kinds of strain: You've got elastic, you've got plastic, and you've got brittle. Just the names alone indicate probably what we're going to be talking about here. I mean, just elastic—the term elastic and plastic and brittle. But what I want to do is to sort of look at those a little bit more closely because there's something that goes on that most people really don't think about. Let's take elastic strain first. Remember now, in order for this to happen, we assume we've already exceeded the strength of whatever this stuff is. Here's an important point: Once you exceed the strength of material, the first response is always, always, always elastic. Before any of the others, the first one is always elastic. Now, here's what *elastic strain* is all about. Just picture this, now, happening. You take whatever this stuff is, you apply a force, it absorbs the energy, and deforms. Remember now, *deformation* is simply a change in size and/or shape. So, whatever this stuff is it deformed—and as long as you keep applying that force, the energy becomes stored in the stuff itself. That's the important part about elastic strain: You store energy. As long as you keep applying that stress, the energy will continue to be stored in whatever it is. As soon as you release the stress, the object or whatever it is goes back to its original shape, releases the energy, and that energy can be used to do work.

Case in point: The best example of an elastic thing that I can think of is a *gum band*—that's a Pittsburgh term for a *rubber band*. Picture taking a rubber band and pulling it out. What we've down now is we've applied a tensional force. As a result, the rubber band has absorbed the energy and deformed—it certainly has changed size and shape. All the energy that you applied to pulling that gum band out is now stored in the band itself, and it will remain stored in there as long as I hold the other end of the rubber band. But note: As soon as I let the rubber band go, what happens? It goes back to its original shape, releases the energy, and the energy can be used to do work— in this case, to fire the gum band across the room someplace. But note: If you were to go over there and pick up that gum band and hold it, it looks like it did before anything happened. And that's one of the characteristics of *elastic deformation*. After it's all said and done, there's no indication that anything had ever happened.

Let me give you some other examples because there are so many of these, and I like to give these in class because it really fixes it in people's minds. Think now, of all the sports that you play that are based upon *elastic response*—and, of course, the one that just pops into my mind, right off the bat, is tennis. Here your opponent fires his tennis ball across the net at you, and you swing at it as hard as you can and hit this tennis ball. Now, if you can see the impact of your racquet and the ball at the moment of impact, the strings on the tennis racquet deform—they change size and shape; the ball flattens out—changes size and shape; all the energy that you whacked into that is now stored in the strings of your racquet and in that ball momentarily. But then, the strings go back to the original shape, the ball goes back to the original shape, and the ball goes across the net to your opponent. So, that's a classic example of an elastic response. For example, at the end of the game, you look at your racquet, it looks like it did before you started. No indication that you ever played. The ball? It looks like it did before you started: There's no indication you ever played. That's characteristic of elastic responses.

Just one more. Another good example would be baseball. Here's a little bit of tweak to this one. Picture now, hitting a baseball. Well, the ball deforms—not as much as the tennis ball did because it's of different stuff, a little bit different structure, you see, but it does deform—it has to—and the bat does indeed "bend," if you will: There is some flexure to it. If you overdo it, of course, the bat breaks, you see: So there is some flexure to it. So as you hit that ball with that bat, you're storing energy in the bat, you're storing energy in the ball, they're both deformed, they both go back to the original shape—and, of course, the ball goes out in the field.

Here's a point while we're talking about stress and strain. Let's say, for example, you were playing baseball, and you hit the ball with a perfect non-rotational compression. Question: What kind of hit do you think you're going to get? Well, if you picture that, probably a line drive, hopefully right out through the infield out into the outfield. On the other hand, let's say you look down to that third-base coach, and he tells you he wants you to pop this thing up over the infield into the short outfield. Here's what you do: You stand up to the plate now, and what you do, you want to hit it again, compression, but you want a little bit of rotational compression now. So you hit it a little bit under the ball, and if you do it right, it will pop it right over the infield into the short outfield. Now, if you do it a little bit too much, it's going to pop it right straight up in the air, and, of course, the catcher's going to catch it, so that's bad. On the other hand, if you look down to the third base coach, and he says, "Lay it down," so what you do now—again, rotational compression—is you simply hit it a little bit high, it goes down, and you've got a bunt. So the point is when you stand up there as a batter, how good you are as a batter is dependent upon how critically you can control those compressional forces with which you hit that ball. And that's all it's about. I was never very good at that. I did a lot of pop-ups when I was a kid, so I was never very good at bat. But anyway, that would be a good example.

One last one: wind-up clocks and wind-up watches. Now, most of us don't have wind-up watches anymore—they're all sort of electronically controlled. If you picture now, a wind-up clock: wind, wind, wind, wind. Inside, there's a spring that you're deforming. It's closing up like that, and then if you stop winding, it unwinds again, and as it unwinds, the energy is being released—elastic response, you see—it's what drives the clock. So, all of those would be examples of an elastic performance. Note the important thing in elastic strain. You apply energy. It absorbs and stores the energy, but then it gives it back to you, and you can use it for whatever you want to do with it—okay, so much for elastic.

Now, here's the point, though. There's a limit as to how much energy any material in the elastic phase can hold. It's called the *elastic limit*. Every material in its elastic phase will only store so much, and after you reach the elastic limit, then and only then can it respond either by *plastic deformation* or *brittle deformation*. But you have to exceed the elastic limit. So, let's take a good example of a plastic stuff. The very best one I can think of would be modeling clay. Everybody's done this: You've got a little ball of modeling clay, and you've got it in your hand, and if you just very carefully do that with it, you can feel the elasticity of this clay ball. In other words, just squeeze and bouncing back, and you've got to be very careful, but if you do it very carefully, it's responding like an elastic stuff. But the point is with modeling clay, the secret of it is, the elastic limit is very, very, very low. So, you're not going to go very far like that before it starts to deform. So, let's just do it. Let's say we take this piece of modeling clay, and we're going to purposely just go beyond the elastic limit, and just squeeze it like that. And you can just feel what's happening: It's gushing under your fist like that. And you open your hand up, and now what does it look like? Well, it looks like the inside of your fist. Did it break? No, no. So it can't be brittle response. It's a plastic response. Why? Why didn't it bounce back? Well, there's no energy to bounce back. Why? Because the characteristic of a *plastic deformation* is the energy is absorbed, the stuff is deformed, and the energy is consumed, rearranging all that stuff, so that's the important word in plastic deformation. There's a *consumption* of whatever energy you apply to it. The reason why it can't bounce back is because you've already used up all the energy, you see. Note: Plastic deformation is permanent: Once it's done, that's it. And that's the reason why you can use modeling clay to make a bust or whatever, and you can come back 10 years later, and it looks the same way as it did when you finished it, because the deformation that you employed was a plastic deformation, and it's simply permanent.

Let's talk about brittle. This is sort of an interesting one. So, in order to explain really what brittle's all about: *Brittle* means that once you exceed that elastic limit, what's going to happen is the stuff that you're talking about is going to break. That's what brittle things do: They break. Now, the real question is "Why?" Hmm. So, to explain why, what I'd like to do is I'd like to go back and talk about another elastic response of stuff. I want to go back and talk about the ringing of a bell. The ringing of a bell is an elastic response. So, here's the deal: You have a bell, and when that clapper hits the inside of the bell, what happens? The energy of the impact is absorbed by the bell. It does deform—it does change size and shape. You can't really see it, but it really does. And as it goes back to its original shape, the energy that it stored briefly is given off, and it's given off in the form of a shock wave, which comes to your ear and is interpreted by your ear as a sound. But note the important thing is that it's a surface thing we're talking about here. If you think about bells—you've all listened to a bell choir. What the bells do—they all have a different tone. And really the reason why they all sound different is because they all have a different size, and what that means is they all have a different surface area. So, whenever the energy is absorbed by the bell and given off, it's given off from the surface now, but the surface area is different in each case. So, as a result, the tone of the bell sounds different: For example, if it's a little bell, it tinkles; if it's a big bell, it bongs. So, then, the sound that you get back is really sort of a function of the shape of the bell and the total surface area. But note: That is, in fact, what the response is. It's simply an elastic response to the clapping of the inside with that clapper.

All right. Well, let's consider another bell. This time let's consider a flat bell, and the flat bell I have in mind is a plate. That's a flat bell. Let's make this really heart-wrenching: The plate I'm thinking about is a family heirloom. I mean, this plate, now, has been in your family for hundreds of years. And you're washing it very carefully, and you're drying it very carefully, and something distracts you, and you drop it. It heads to the floor. Now, it hits the floor, absorbs energy, deforms, stores the energy for a while, and then releases it. How do you know—without even looking down—how do you know that it didn't break? The sound of a ringing bell, it's what it is—it's a flat bell. In other words, the idea in that little scenario was when the plate hit the floor it absorbed the energy; it did deform—if you could really see it up close and personal; it stored the energy, but did not exceed the elastic limit. So the energy was given off again as the result of a tone, as the sound of a ringing bell. So you don't even have to look down to know you lucked out. So what you do is you get the plate, put that thing away, and hope no one takes it out again for another 10 years. You see—you don't want to mess with that thing again.

Let's say, on the other hand, what you did was, when you dropped it, it hit the floor a little bit too hard. It absorbed the energy, it did deform, it stored energy up to the elastic limit, but then you exceeded the elastic limit, and it broke. How do you know, without even looking down, that it broke? It's the sound of ringing bells again. Now there's more than one bell. Let's say it broke into three or four pieces. Now, note what you've got. You've got three or four bells of different sizes and shapes. They all have different surface areas. So when the energy is given off it's going to be different tones from each one of those ringing bells, and it's that melding, that melding of the sound from those ringing bells at different tones that is the sound of breaking glass. And every time I go through this in class—I just did—I just shudder. Why? Because I'm reminded of one of the many jobs I had in college I was a wait. And of all the things I've ever done in my life the only job I truly hated was as a wait. You're always fearful of that tray you're carrying—of dropping it. You know what you do? When you hear somebody drops a tray in a restaurant, at least in a college town, everybody cheers and claps. No, you shouldn't do that. And if it ever happens to you, don't ever do that. I always thought what you ought to do is just walk over to this poor person and give them a big hug just to let them know they're still loved. Because that's a terrible, terrible thing for a wait—God only knows, it happened enough for me. As a matter of fact, I think that's why I was fired. But anyway, so that's breaking.

But the real question to be answered is: "Why did it break in the first place?" Let's go back to the ringing bell. It dropped to the floor, hit the floor, absorbed energy, stored it, did not exceed the elastic limit, and gave it back off again. But let's say it hit the floor, absorbed the energy, deformed, but you did exceed the elastic limit. How is the energy given off? The energy, remember, is given off from the surface. It's a surface thing. The problem is the amount of energy you tried to store in this plate, or whatever it is, was more than could be given off from the surface. What you need is some more surface area. So how are you going to get more surface area? Well, you just break. Note: If you break something, now, you do have additional surface area. The additional surface area is the edges of the pieces. So, the idea is that is why things break. The reason why things break is to give more surface area to get rid of the energy that you couldn't store beyond the elastic limit.

With that in mind, let's just consider this again. Let's say when a plate or something hits the floor, let's say you exceed the elastic limit just by a teense, just a little bit. All you need is just the slightest amount of new surface area. What do you think is going to happen? Will it shatter into a thousand pieces? No, I don't think so. Probably what's going to happen is it's going to crack. That's what cracks are. I mean, they're breaks. They're surface area. So, the idea is if you don't need an awful lot of surface area added, maybe you simply have a crack form. And that's what cracks are—cracks in cups, or glasses, or whatever. That's simply the little bit of surface area that you needed beyond what you had. So, maybe you'll just get a crack. Then, you see, if that was your heirloom plate then you really put it away in a place where no one can find it anymore. But let's say it hit the floor, a little bit more surface area, it might break into two or three pieces.

Note: Let's say it wasn't a question of hitting the floor. Let's say you threw it at your brother, and it missed him and hit the wall. Then it would break into what my sainted mother would call "smithereens." Why were there so many pieces? Well, pretty simple: you had a lot of energy you had to get rid of. What you needed was a lot of surface area addition, and that's why you had more pieces. The more energy you have to release, the more pieces there are. So, you see, that is what breaking is all about. *Breaking* is simply providing that surface area that you had to have to get rid of that the original material did not have up until after you exceeded the elastic limit.

There's what elastic, plastic, and brittle are all about. If you just sort of review in your mind, here are the big points, now. Elastic response: You absorb energy, you store it, and you release it, and if it's elastic, the material you're talking about can store whatever you put into it. You do not exceed this elastic limit. So, that's the important thing about elastic materials: the absorbing, the storing, and the releasing of energy in a form that you can do work with. Plastic: You absorb the energy, you consume it internally, and so it's permanent deformation. That's plastic. Brittle is: You absorb energy, you exceed the elastic limit, you need some more surface area to get rid of it, so it breaks in order to give the surface area you need to release it. Obviously, breaking—brittle fracture—is also permanent.

Now, here's a question: How about rocks? Do rocks respond elastically, plastically, and brittlely? Well, yeah, they do. For example, in the next lecture we're going to talk about folds. Well, you drive along the highway, and you see sometimes an entire fold in a rock outcrop, or perhaps in a hillside. And what that is—here you have a plastic response. Picture taking a piece of clay and rolling it out into a flat layer and pushing it together: You can form folds like that. If you look at that little folded piece of clay, is it broken? No, no, it's not broken. There are no cracks in it, so it's not brittle response. Did it snap back when you let it go? No, it stayed folded like that. So it has to be plastic because there are only three kinds. When you look at rocks in hillsides, if you see these folds as you drive along, when were they created? I'm thinking just around this area itself, the folds in the Appalachians were created somewhere around 250 to 300 million years ago, and here they are today. They didn't snap back. Why? It was a permanent deformation. So, yes: The folds we are going to talk about in the very next lecture would be an example of a plastic response.

How about brittle? Are there brittle responses? Yeah, the two big ones, of course, are going to be faults and joints. Now we're going to find out that the big difference between them is simply whether or not there has been any movement. By definition a *fault* is a break in the Earth's crust where there has been movement. In the case of a *joint*, it's a break in the Earth's crust during which there has been no appreciable or measurable movement. Just based upon what we've said, the joint, now, looks to me like it's a crack. It looks to me like what happened to this rock: It was subjected to energy that was stored and exceeded the elastic limit, but just a little bit. All you needed was a little bit more surface area to release that energy, and that's what a joint is all about. So we'll talk about joints in two lectures from now, but basically that's the way to look at joints. They're simply the response of this brittle rock where you didn't really have to generate an awful lot more surface area.

On the hand now, if it's a fault: A fault basically is a break where you have had appreciable movement. Obviously, you had to release, and did release, an awful lot of energy. Some of the energy was used to actually move the rocks along the fault. And I think I'll save what you did with the other energy until the right time comes—because I want to keep you coming back, you see. We'll talk about what happened to the rest of that energy that was released in another lecture.

But how about this elastic response? I mean, come on, do rocks snap back? Well, yeah, they do. Let me set a scenario for you. What I want you to do is I want you to consider Canada. And I want you to consider Canada up until about 2 million years ago. Up until that time, Canada probably looked pretty much like Canada does now. But what happened 2 million years ago? Well, 2 million years ago snow started falling into the interior of Canada. And it fell, and it fell, and it fell, and it was transformed into glacial ice. So, over the center of Canada, this huge ice sheet started to form—and it started to move out in all directions. It moved north to the Arctic Ocean until it ran into the Arctic, and it moved all the way over to the Atlantic until it ran into the Atlantic. It moved westward all the way over to the Rocky Mountains—actually it ran about 5,000 feet up onto the front range of the Rocky Mountains. Then it moved to the south. It came to the south about as far as the Ohio River Valley: As a matter of fact, the present course of the Ohio River would have been about the leading edge of this ice sheet. So, anyway, that started about 2 million years ago.

And then starting somewhere maybe 20,000 to 30,000 years ago, things started melting back. And from this particular area we're talking about, under this ice sheet now, picture what's happening.

That whole area of Canada under that ice sheet was simply bowed down under the weight of the ice. Note a very important thing: This is the lithosphere we're talking about bowing down—remember, under the lithosphere is the asthenosphere. The reason why it was able to bow down is because the rocks of the asthenosphere being plastic and being able to flow, flowed out from underneath of this weighted, now, lithosphere. So we have a bowing down of the lithosphere under this huge sheet of ice. How huge was huge? I really don't know. You're talking about the ice sheet over Antarctica is about 10,000 feet thick. Who knows what this thing was? It could have been 20,000 feet thick. But, anyway, here's this bowing down of the lithosphere, now. Then what happened about 10,000 years ago, I guess it was, the ice finally moved back from that part of the world and retreated back up to Greenland—that's about all that's left of that once-great ice sheet. But basically here's this depression now. Here's this depression in the lithosphere. What happened? Water flowed in from the North Atlantic and filled it. And so what did it form? It formed Hudson Bay.

Question: That deformation that occurred under that ice? Was it brittle? Well, from what we can tell looking in the area there is no indication there was any breaking of rocks—so no, no, it wasn't brittle. So it was either plastic, or it was elastic. Which one of those? Well, note: If it was plastic, it's permanent, and it would stay that way, and—as a result—Hudson Bay is going to be there—well, I can't say forever: Nothing lasts forever; but for a long, long, long time. On the other hand, if it was elastic deformation what is going to happen is that whole area is slowly going to rise and go back to its original position. Remember, that is what happens in elastic responses. There's no indication anything had ever happened. Well, I guess you'll have to take my word for this, but as we speak, as far as we know, the area under Hudson Bay is slowly, slowly rising. A student asked me one time, "Why is it so slow? I mean, the ice has been gone for 10,000 years." The rate at which that area is rising is really being controlled by how fast the rocks can flow back under it in that asthenosphere. Now, it's plastic, it's flowing, but pretty slowly. But, nevertheless, this area is slowly on the rise, and so if it continues—always the big "if"—if it continues, it will go right back to where it was. What's going to happen? Hudson Bay will drain back into the North Atlantic from whence it came, and you'll never know anything happened. There'll never be any indication, as far as depression goes, that there ever had been an ice sheet up there—because that is the response of elastic things.

So, anyway, do rocks respond elastically? Yeah. Now that's on a very grand scale. There's one other example of an elastic response of rocks, and again, I think I'm going to keep that for a while because it's going to become a very important part of another lecture, and again: I've got to keep you coming back. So, we'll talk about that in another lecture.

Lecture Twenty-Eight
The Geologic Structures

Scope:

The three basic rock structures are *folds, faults,* and *joints.* Throughout our travels, we sometimes observe rocks that are bent into folds. They can appear on any scale, from the intricate swirls in a slab of marble on a tabletop to a massive outcropping of granite exposed in the side of a mountain. Cracks—called joints—are also readily observable in rocks. And who has not heard of the San Andreas Fault? Folds are of three basic types: *monoclines, anticlines,* and *synclines.* Their differences depend on orientation. Their surface features can be categorized based on a further set of parameters that have to do with angle and orientation. Finally, the shape of a fold can be identified—based on angle and orientation—as *symmetrical, asymmetrical, overturned,* or *recumbent.* Each of these categories reflects the degree of severity and duration of the original compressive force.

Outline

I. Rock structures form as a result of the application of stress beyond the strength of the rock. The three basic rock structures are *folds, faults,* and *joints.*

   A. Folds result from compression. When you fold something, you reduce its size. Models also involve a reduction of size, both in dimensions and in material strength. As mentioned earlier, a *flume* is a model used to study how streams pick up and transport material. The theory of laminar flow was the result of flume experiments.

   1. Geological models are built to gather data and form theories.

   2. Anyone can model a fold by simply pushing the opposite sides of a sheet of paper toward each other, which generates a non-rotational compressive force. The trend of the fold is perpendicular to the force.

   3. When you do the same thing with a ream of paper, the same thing happens, but some sheets move across each other. This happens in nature, for example, with shale.

The grooves, or striations, thus formed are called *slickensides* and form parallel to the applied force.

4. Special modeling clay, called *Kaolinite clay*, has been used to test folding and faulting in an apparatus called a *clay cake table*. Much data have been gathered that way, though such modeling has had its critics.

5. Nowadays, modeling is done with computer programs to discover, for example, what generates Earth's magnetic field or why the magnetic field reverses from time to time.

B. There are three types of folds: *monoclines*, *anticlines*, and *synclines*, all formed from compression.

1. The simplest of the three types of folds is the monocline: The rocks slope in one direction. Monoclines commonly form around the margins of local or regional uplifts or above zones where rocks have been broken and displaced vertically along faults. The edge of the Colorado Plateau is an example.

2. Anticlines and synclines are almost always associated with each other. The anticline is an up-warp in Earth's crust, while a syncline is the adjacent down-warp.

C. Several basic parameters are used to describe folds, including the *amplitude* of the fold, the orientation of the *axial plane*, the *strike* and *dip* of the *limbs* of the fold, the strike of the *fold axis*, and the *plunge* of the fold axis.

1. The amplitude of the fold is simply the distance between the top of the anticline to the base of the adjoining syncline. The amplitude is determined by the duration or strength of compressive forces.

2. The axial plane is an imaginary plane, drawn parallel to the fold, that attempts to bisect the fold.

3. The limbs of the fold refer to the rocks that dip *away* from the axis of the anticline or toward the axis of the adjoining syncline.

4. Strike and dip are used to describe any planar surface, such as axial planes or limbs. The strike is the direction of the line of intersection of the plane and the horizontal relative to the north geographic pole. Dip is the angle between the plane and the horizontal, measured perpendicular to the strike and identified by direction.

5. The fold axis is the line of intersection between the axial plane and the limbs of the fold.

6. The plunge of a fold is the angle between the axis and the horizontal. Folds come to an end by "plunging."

II. Based on the angle and direction of dip of the limbs relative to the axial plane, folds are described as: *symmetrical, asymmetrical, overturned,* and *recumbent.*

A. A symmetrical fold is one where the axial plane is vertical, and the limbs dip away from the axial plane in opposite directions at the same angle of dip. In general, symmetrical folds are generated by horizontal non-rotational compression, with increased compression resulting in an increase in fold amplitude and a concurrent decrease in the distance between adjacent axial planes.

B. In asymmetrical folds, the axial plane inclines, and the limbs dip away from the axial plane but at different angles of dip. Most asymmetric folds form by horizontal rotational compression, with continued compression resulting in an increase in asymmetry as the axial plane is tipped in the direction of maximum compressional force.

C. An overturned fold is one in which the axial plane inclines, and the limbs dip in the same direction as the axial plane. Overturned folds are the result of continued deformation of asymmetrical folds.

D. A recumbent fold is one in which the axial plane approaches the horizontal. Recumbent folds form under the most extreme conditions of folding.

E. Most of the great mountains of the world are referred to as *foldbelt mountains* because folds are a major component of their overall structures. An example of a foldbelt mountain range is the Appalachian Mountains.

1. We can determine how the Appalachians formed by examining *physiographic provinces,* that is, regions of common rock types, structures, history, and topography. For the Appalachians, these provinces are labeled, from east to west, as follows: Piedmont, Blue Ridge, Great Valley or Shenandoah, Valley and Ridge, High Plateau, and Low Plateau.

2. The folds exposed in the Appalachians show a progressive change in style from east to west.
3. The easternmost folding, the Piedmont, is a highly deformed recumbent folding.
4. Westward, the folds reflect a decrease in compressional intensity, with overturned folds in the Blue Ridge Province and highly asymmetric folds in the Valley and Ridge Province. Further west, in the High Plateau, the folds are symmetrical but with high amplitude.
5. By the time we reach the far western Low Plateau, the amplitude is very small; the limbs of the fold have only a $2°$ to $3°$ slope—basically, horizontal. This shows that the energy came from east to west.
6. What made the systematic change from east to west? From our knowledge of plate tectonics, we know that the continent-to-continent collision that created the supercontinent of Pangea was what created the Appalachians.

Recommended Reading:

Twiss, R. J., and E. M. Moores, *Structural Geology*.

Davis, G. H., and S. J. Reynolds, *Structural Geology of Rocks and Regions*.

Questions to Consider:

1. What would be the order in which the various kinds of folds will develop under continued application of compressional stress?
2. Under what geologic scenario would folds be expected to form?

Lecture Twenty-Eight—Transcript
The Geologic Structures

In this lecture, we're going to talk about kinds of structures. Now, there are three basic kinds: folds, faults, and joints. In this lecture it will be folds: We'll talk about the plastic deformation in this particular lecture. And then in the next one, we're going to talk about the brittle, mainly the faults and the joints. Before I get into that, I want to talk a little bit about modeling. Now, a lot of us have done modeling. As a kid I built model airplanes, for example. And this is a good example of what modeling is all about. Consider making a model airplane: What you're going to do is to make a small reproduction of something that's much, much larger, you see. So you're reducing the size. Now, you don't just reduce the size, you also have to reduce the strength of the materials that you're going to be using. Everything has to be downsized, if you will. Think about the aircraft, now, made of aluminum. What do you make this model out of? Well, you make it out of a combination of balsa wood and tissue paper. So we've downsized the material's strength, you see. Well, that's not all. I mean, you look over at that aircraft, and it's got these big engines on it. Well, we have to downsize the energy from the engine system. So, what did I downsize it to when I was kid?—to rubber bands. But here you have a model: It's reduced in size, it's reduced in material strengths, it's reduced in—in this case—energy source, but it does the same thing the big guy did. It still flies. It's very important, you see, to do modeling like that.

Well, in geology, we do modeling, and the idea is this: If you look out in nature, there are things out there—mountain building, perhaps, or whatever you'd like to be able to sort of re-create what was going on somehow in the laboratory, if you will, because you see the end products out there. You see the end products of folds, and faults, and stuff, but you want to know, "How did they get that way?" Well, that's really what modeling is all about. For example, we already talked about one model. We were talking about streams, and I mentioned to you, for example, that we have in the business a thing called a *flume*. What it was, it's sort of a racetrack, and we run water around it. That's sort of a model, now, of a stream. The one I built, for example, was about 30 feet long and about 15 feet wide. The individual stream itself was about 2 feet wide and, as I remember, 1½ feet deep. So, obviously, it's a reduction in size and also in shape, because I don't know too many streams that run in a circle like that. The idea was, here, what we wanted to do, was to learn something about what happens at the base of the stream—what happens in the channel? It's pretty tough to go out there into an actual stream and get down there in the channel, seeing what's being picked up and what's being moved—especially if the stream is either highly turbulent, or if it's just murky with sediment. So, anyway, we build a model. So, that would have been an example.

Well, the results of that. Well, for example, we talked about that little chart that we had plotted with velocity versus turbulence and particle size across the bottom. Now, the data that generated that plot came from experiments done with flumes like this. It wasn't my data, but it was somebody else's. But the idea was, remember, the things we learned. Well, the things we learned—remember, there was a point at which the up arrow and down arrow were equal to each other? In other words, the force of turbulence was equal to the force of gravity: At that point, or just beyond it, the particle should have been picked off the bottom and moved, and wasn't. See, we learned that from flume experiments. We found out that you actually have to add a little bit more energy beyond that which is theoretically required to get the thing off the bottom and move. So, that's the way we learned that. And we learned that it was true for pebbles, and granules, and sand. But how about those really fine jobs down there? How about the clay and the silt?

We had to come up with some idea—the flume experiments were saying you can't run this thing fast enough to get those things off by themselves. So there was a theory that had to be evolved. What was it? Well, that's way they came up with this whole idea of the laminar flow. The *laminar flow*—the idea of that laminar layer—that was the result of flume experiments like these, when it was finally decided the reason why those fine particles were so difficult to get off the bottom, the reason why you had to add the amount of energy needed for a pebble or a granule just to get those things off the bottom, was because they totally were residing in this very, very thin layer called a *laminar layer*. Now, it's a theory. No one's ever seen the laminar layer. No one ever will see the laminar layer. Note what a *theory* is: It's a scientifically sound idea—and I think that is—that explains what you see. And that's what we saw: It took so much energy to get those fine particles off the ground. Anyway, that would be an example of a model, and a lot of information that we understand now about how streams do their thing is gotten from very simple models like that.

Another question: How about these structures we're talking about? Can we model some of these structures? We're going to talk about folds, for example. All right, let's talk about modeling a fold. Here's all you have to do—and we do this, for example, in the Geology 1 Lab with the students to give them some kind of a feeling for how folds form. So here would be a very, very simple model. You simply take a piece of paper on a table, and here's all you do with it. You push the edges together like that. Note: You have a fold—we'll name it a little bit later—but you have a fold. What can you tell? What should the student see? Well, note: The student should see that we're talking about compressive forces here. You can't form a fold with tensional forces: Just try it with a piece of paper. You'll pull it apart: It's impossible. So, right off the bat, the students should see that we're talking, here, about compressive forces and note: non-rotational compression forces in this case, non-rotational compression. Here's something else they should see: Note the length of the fold. The fold is perpendicular—the trend of the fold is perpendicular to the forces. Do you see that out there in nature? Sure, you go out in nature, and you see folds out there, and what you see are long, linear folds, and how do we interpret them? If they're symmetrical and cross-sectional like that one was, we interpret it being it was a non-rotational compressive force, and the forces came perpendicular to the trend of the fold. This is something that happened 250 million years ago, but we can interpret what it was like back then just from the shape and the orientation of the fold. So, that would be a good model. But note: In this little experiment, this was just, let's say, one layer of rock.

How about if you wanted to model, let's say, a number of layers of sedimentary rock stacked on top of each other? Could you do it with paper like that? Yeah, you know what I would do—I would take a ream of paper. You put a ream of paper down, now, and just push the edge of the ream together. The same thing will happen—it will form into that *symmetrical fold* that we just saw. The fold trend will be perpendicular to the compressive forces. But here's something else you'll note: If you watch very closely, what you'll see as those pieces of paper bend and move, they'll sort of move across each other like that. There's actually motion between each piece of paper and the one above and below. Question: Is that happening out there in nature? Let's go out and see. If you went out to a fold—and this is especially true of shales (that's why we look at them because shales are very soft, and this is very prevalent among shales)—so, let's say you had two shale layers. As it folds, you see, they sort of move on each other like that. If you look at the surface of those shale layers, they're going to form little striations or grooves: We call them *slickensides*. Note the orientation is always sort of parallel to the direction the rocks were moving against each other—not perpendicular, do you see? So here, these striations are going to be basically parallel to the applied forces. So what you see in the lab, actually you can see out in the field. That's what modeling is all about.

Well, paper is one thing. But, for example, could I, say, model faulting with a piece of paper or a ream of paper? No. So you have to go to some other material. So what we went to—and the one everybody used—was modeling clay. It was a special kind of modeling clay. Actually you had to make your own. What we found was best is there's a particular clay called *Kaolinite*—which you don't have to worry about—but *Kaolinite clay*. We mixed it with water, and we mixed it to make a certain consistency to it. Then what we would do, we had a table—it was called a *clay cake table*, because we had a clay cake, you see. And we put this clay cake on the table. One part of the table had a barrier, and we put one edge of the clay cake up against it. And the other had a barrier that could be moved. So, again, all we did was take this clay cake. This barrier could be moved either by hand or by a screw of some kind, or by motor—and the idea is, you can do exactly the same thing with a clay cake as you did with the paper. Now, here's an important point: Depending upon what you want to do, let's say we wanted to do a fold. Remember, fold is plastic deformation. What we did is we mixed the clay that was very, well, back in like making a dough, very thin you see—we wanted it to hold its shape, but we wanted it to be able to flow because that's what folds are. So we make up a special kind of clay with quite a bit of water in it, more water than normal. And what happens when you compress that? The same kind of folds will form that we did with a piece of paper—except now, it's a little bit more realistic. We can put, if you we want to have layers, you can do that. You put a layer of clay down, make another roll out of layer, put a stack of layers on top of each other.

Note: If we wanted to, say, model a fault: We want to break this thing now. Well, you see, the consistency of that kind of clay is too fluid. It'll bend—it's plastic deformation—but now, we want it to break. What we would do would be to take another kind of batch of clay, would add more clay minerals in with it. It would get a little stiffer now than before. So now, when we compress it, rather than flowing, it would break. So, you see, the kind of stuff you pick, basically, is depending upon what you're trying to model. The bottom line is that there was an awful lot of work done with these clay models, and I was involved in that years ago. We got an awful lot of information about what went on in mountain building. Like I say, what you see in a mountain range—the Appalachians, the Himalaya: I don't care which one it is—you see the end product of the deformational history. What I want to know is: Can I explain what I see out there that's the end product? How did it get that way? A lot of our information was gotten by these models. There were a lot of people who were anti-model. The reason why: Whenever you scale down—you see, we're scaling down size—one of the problems is they used to say, "Well, you're not really scaling down the strength of material because that clay is too strong. If you really scaled everything down, let's say, to that size, you're going to have to use something a lot weaker in strength than clay." And see—that was their argument. A lot of people tried. They used, for example, Jell-O™. Even I tried that one: It didn't work very well. Anyway, so there were a lot of people who wouldn't accept it. On the other hand, there were those of us who said, "I understand the shortcomings of this, but we got information that seemed to be duplicating what's out there in nature." And that's all we wanted to do anyway. So, anyway: This whole idea of modeling was a big thing.

We don't do much in the way of clay modeling anymore, but we still model. How? Computer modeling. Computer modeling is a big, big thing nowadays. All you need is someone who's really smart enough to write some kind of a mathematical relationship, you see, to describe whatever it is you're going to do. And then you need someone who's sharp enough to write the program to do it. But we're always modeling things now. You see all kinds of computer modeling. For example, here's what we're modeling a lot of: Right now, a big emphasis on modeling is, let's say, the core. We're modeling the core of Earth. Why? Well, we know it's molten—the seismologists told us that a long time ago. But here's some things we

59

don't quite understand. For example, where does this magnetic field come from? Back when I took geology first and throughout my career, I simply tell students, as it rotates—as the solid part—the mantle—rotates around this liquid core—there's a dynamo effect. "What's dynamo effect?" Well, I'm not really sure what that means.

See, we don't understand, even today, where this magnetic field came from. So, they're trying to model, now, what really does go on within this liquid core that would possibly generate a magnetic field like that. And here's the other thing we still really don't understand. Why does it flip? We talked about those magnetic reversals—well, there are times when the magnetic field of the Earth switches: The North Pole becomes the South Pole; the South Pole becomes the North Pole. And the important thing is this doesn't happen really slowly over a period of several million years. This happens like geologically right now. Now it's switched. Now it's switched back. Now it's switched. Why? What's causing that reversal? I don't think anybody knows that answer. The answer may lie in those modeling experiments they're doing on the core in the mantle. There's an awful lot of work still going on in modeling, it's just that we're using different tools now than we did before. Okay, so much for modeling.

Let's go on to a discussion, now, of folds. Folds are all formed from compression—that's point number one. You cannot form a fold, for example, with a piece of paper: Try to pull it out. You're not going to do any folding pulling it out under tension. So, they're all formed as a result of compression. There are basically three different kinds of folds: the *monocline*, the *anticline*, and the *syncline*. Now monocline, *mono* means one. A monocline is basically a single sloping curve like that: a fold that simply has one side to it, if you will. Where do you see these? Very commonly, they develop where you have some kind of a major uplift. Now, we've talked an awful lot, for example, about the forces that lifted the Colorado Plateau 10 billion years ago to where it is now. When it lifted it up, remember, inside the Colorado Plateau there was no deformation at all to speak of. Where the deformation is, is along the outside edge: If you go around the outside edge of the Colorado Plateau, what you'll see are sedimentary rocks sort of just draped down over the edge forming *monoclinal folds*. So, that would be an example of a monocline.

The two big ones, however, are *anticlines* (an "up-warp") and a *syncline* (which is a "down-warp"). Now, you can have an anticline all by itself, or I guess you could have a syncline all by itself. I've never seen one like that. Wherever they form under compression you have them in sets: anticline, syncline, anticline, syncline—like that. Here's a question students always ask, "Where's the anticline start and end?" I guess you could say the anticline starts at the bottom of the syncline to the bottom of the next syncline. "Well, how about the syncline?" It starts at the top of the anticline to the top of the next anticline. But that's not how we do it. We simply say, "The anticline is the up-warp in the Earth's crust; the syncline is the down-warp in the Earth's crust." So, anyway, those are the three basic kinds.

Now, what I'd like to do is talk a little bit about some of the basic parameters we use to describe these things. Let's say, for example, amplitude. Remember when I did that little experiment about pushing that paper together, it sort of bowed up like that, made a symmetrical fold. Well, the height of the that—the height from the top of the fold to the bottom of the fold—basically, that's the *amplitude*. It's simply measured in feet. What's the significance of it? Just think about this: If we took that piece of paper and did the experiment again—and, again, in lab I used to have my students do this—at first, as you start pushing them together the first amplitude obviously has to start out small, and as you continue to push, the amplitude grows greater, and greater, and greater. In other words, the fold increases in amplitude. Significance: What is it telling you? Well, what it's really saying is the longer you apply the force, or, perhaps, the greater force you apply, the greater the amplitude is going to be. So, if you go out in nature, and you look at a series of folds, and the amplitude is changing within this area, you can use the amplitude of the fold to tell which of those was being worked on the longest or with the most intense energy, and which had the least. So, you see, that's a pretty important thing—the amplitude, so we pay a lot of attention to the amplitude.

The next one is a thing called the axial plane. What the *axial plan* is, it's an imaginary plane that attempts to divide the fold along its length into two equal halves. We'll see the significance of the axial plane whenever we start talking about different kinds of folds. But that's basically what it is. It's just an imaginary plane that's drawn parallel to the length of the fold, which divides it in two equal halves. Another thing are the *limbs*: We talk about the limbs of the fold. The limbs of the fold are simply the rocks that come off the axis of the anticline, or go toward the axis of the syncline—so that's what the limbs are.

One of the things we have to describe on the limbs, however, is their attitude in three-dimensional space. So, we have a measure we call *strike and dip*. This is pretty important because there are all kinds of planar features out there. The limbs of a fold, of course, are a planar feature. A fault surface is a planar feature. A layer of rock is a planar feature. So if you want to describe this particular plane, let's say, to someone else and have them picture it clearly in their mind, what you do is you measure what we call strike and dip. So here's what it is: first of all, the strike. The *strike* is the intersection between the plane and the horizontal. Note that's a line, and the line has a *direction*. So, you determine the direction of that line. And we determine directions of things relative to the North Pole, and so we say, That line is striking north, or "It's N45°E," or "It's N45°W"— whatever the strike is. So as soon as you tell a listener that, all of a sudden they know, now, which direction the strike is. They can picture this in their mind. So, here we have this plane, and obviously there's a dip to it. The *dip* is simply the angle between the horizontal and the plane. So, you tell the listener again, "The plane is striking, let's say, due north, and it's dipping 45°." Okay, I can visualize that, but there are two possibilities. If this is the strike, the plane could be dipping in that direction, that limb, or, on the other side. How do I know which one of these limbs we're talking about?

The way you do that is: Whenever you give the dip, you tell which direction it's dipping. For example, for simplistic purposes, let's say the strike is due north. And here's one plane. That's dipping to the east. Here's the other one dipping to the west. So, if I told this person, "This plane has a strike of north south, dips 45° to the east, always perpendicular," I don't care where this person is in the world, they can picture that plane in three-dimensional space. And that's what the importance of strike and dip is all about.

Now, the last one. We'll talk about this thing called *plunge*. These folds—when we made that little fold with a piece of paper, it looked like it was going to go on forever, but, of course, folds can't go on forever. So what they end up doing is what we call plunging. Now, here's what *plunging* is. What I would do is I would take that piece of paper again. And now hold the piece of paper down with, say, the backs of your hands and your thumbs, and with your fingers, now, just push those edges together. You'll see what happens is they'll form a fold. Note: You can see the fold on one end, the end away from me. But note: Back here next to me there is no fold—in other words, it's "dying out." It's "coming to an end." It's plunging. That's how folds come to an end. They come to an end by plunging. So what we do is we measure the axis of the fold direction and the angle between the axis, which would be the intersection of the limbs with each other, and the horizontal. So, in other words, that's how all folds come to an end. So, anyway, that would be plunge. So, those are the descriptions we make of all the folds, and if you do that, pretty soon you have a pretty good idea of not only the forces that created this fold, but which direction they came from and how long the forces acted along the fold. Okay, so much for the parameters.

Now, let's finally get around to the different kinds. Let's say we take, for example, the simplest possibility. We're going to take, now, a picture applying non-rotational compression. Picture now, as you do that, what's going to happen? The little experiment we did, our very first one. You're going to form a fold, and the description of the fold, now, is going to say the axial plane is vertical. Limbs dip away from the axial plane in opposite directions at equal angles. The cross section is symmetrical: So that would be a *symmetrical fold*. Significance? If you go out and if you see a symmetrical fold, the picture a geologist would have in his mind: This fold formed undoubtedly—probably, at least—from non-rotational compression. And, as a result, it formed simply a symmetrical fold. So that's what symmetrical folds tell us: simply non-rotational compression.

Let me change the scenario a little bit here. Let's say instead of directly non-rotational compression, which would be like if you took your hands, palm down, and just put your fingers together side by side like that. That would be the non-rotational compression. Now, what we're going to do, picture taking your hands and having one above the other, maybe just a little bit, not a lot. Now, you see, if you moved your hands together, one would sort of pass over top of the one below—that would be rotational compression now. So, here's what we're going to do. We're going to have a scenario in which we're going to take our block, and we're going to compress it again but this time under rotational compression. So, back to the block on our clay cake table.

As we start this experiment, the first fold that undoubtedly will form—always does seem to form, at least in my experience—the first fold will be symmetrical. And it may actually increase in amplitude some, but very, very soon, what's going to happen? Picture now, let's say your right hand moving over the top of your left hand. What's going to happen is the fold is going to start changing shape. What's going to happen as you continue to apply the force is the axial plane, now, is going to start tilting over in the direction of your right hand moving across your left. And as the axial plane tips over, what's going to happen to the limbs of the fold, now, they're dipping away from the axis all right, but note: different directions—but different angles. One's steeper than the other, and the steeper one will always be the one that's tipping in the direction in which your right hand is moving over the top of your left. And if you continue to do that, the sequence is as follows. The *asymmetry*, now, of the fold simply starts to change. As we go on and apply more force to it and more energy to it, the axial plane continues to tip over on its side like that. And pretty soon, you're going to get to the point, now, where you have these folds that are asymmetric, and they are going to get to the point where that far limb—the one that's pointing in the direction in which your right hand was moving—that one is now vertical. It's still asymmetric, but then the next point is, it's going to go beyond that point, and now we have the scenario where we have an inclined axial plane, both limbs dipping in the same direction. Now, you see, it's beyond asymmetry now: It's *overturned*. If you continue to go beyond that, what you're going to end up with, ultimately, is that the axial plane and the limbs are going to, as they say, approach the horizontal. We call that *recumbent folds*.

So, note the sequence of events. You start off with symmetrical folds, then you go to *asymmetric folds*, then you go to *overturned folds*, and the ultimate in folding deformation is *recumbency*. Can I give you a really good example of that? Yes, I can. And what I'd like you to think about now is a cross-section of the Appalachians. I use the Appalachians simply because I'm more familiar with it than any other mountain range. But this could apply to any of the major mountain ranges of the world: the Appalachians, the Alps, the Himalaya. It makes no difference. Here's the picture: If you look at the cross-section of the Appalachians what we do is we break it into what we call physiographic provinces. Now, the *physiographic provinces*: That's an area that has common rock types, structures, history, and topography. So if we look at the Appalachians, what you're going to see from the East Coast to the West. As you come off the coastal plain, the first of the provinces you run into is what we call the Piedmont. Let me just tell you what the provinces are first: Now, this will be east to west—you have the Piedmont, then you run into the Blue Ridge Province, and then you run into what we call the Great Valley, which is known locally as the Shenandoah or whatever. Then the next one is the Appalachian Mountains themselves. We call that the Valley and Ridge Province. Here's where you have those long parallel ridges and long parallel valleys. Then the next one in line to the west, you get into the plateau, and then the next one is what I call the *high plateau*. And then, finally, you have what we call the *low plateau*. The western edge of the low plateau probably is somewhere around if you put a line down through westernmost West Virginia, easternmost Ohio, and on down through Kentucky. That probably would be the western edge of the Appalachians.

Now let's go back and look at the folds—just the folds now, we'll ignore the faults at the moment because we're going to see the faults later. If you go to the Piedmont, the first thing you're going to find is you can't find any rocks in the Piedmont. These are highly deformed metamorphic rocks. They weather very, very fast, and as a result are covered with regolith and soil. But if you can get to a quarry—and there are some—and look at it, here's what you're going to see: highly deformed metamorphic rocks. You're going to find volcanic rocks in there, but in terms of the folds highly, highly recumbent folding. I mean, it just looks like a marble-cake kind of thing; just picture that. When you come over, then, to the Blue Ridge, what you see as you cross the Blue Ridge, you see not recumbent folds but overturned folds—pretty highly overturned folds in the Blue Ridge—in other words, not quite the extent of deformation. Once you get into the Great Valley now—here's another place a little hard to find outcrops because it's a limestone valley, and the limestone weathers very fast and is covered with soil—but again, if you go to quarries, here's what you're going to see: You're going to see overturned folds again, but not with the degree of overturning in the Blue Ridge. Then when you get over to the Valley and Ridge, the real mountains—these are the ones you can really see as you drive through on the interstate for example—what you're going to see is that the folds are highly, highly asymmetric. Usually that western limb is almost vertical in almost all the cases. So, they're highly asymmetric now. Once you get up on to the plateau, things change a lot. Once you get up on the plateau—this would be, now, what I would call the high plateau—the folds are symmetrical okay, but high amplitude. The high amplitude—high enough, for example, that they can actually appear on the surface as ridgelines. So if you go with the high plateau you're looking at long parallel ridges and long parallel valleys nowhere near the magnitude of the Valley and Ridge, but they're there because of these symmetrical folds.

Once you go west of that, now, you're into the low plateau. Morgantown, for example, is right at the very eastern edge of the low plateau. In the low plateau, now, you do have folds. They are symmetrical folds, but the amplitudes are very, very small—very, very small amplitudes. They are so small, for example, they do not hold up any ridgelines at all. If you drive from Morgantown west, what the area looks like is just gently rolling hills, but no kind of structural control do you see at the surface. Now, these rocks: As you're driving along, the rocks basically look like they're horizontal. Why? Because we're talking about symmetrical anticlines and synclines with the limbs with the dips of like 2°—maybe 3°. Now, the significance of 2 to 3: Your eye and mine cannot perceive that as sloping. To your eye and mine, a 2° or 3° slope would basically be a horizontal surface. So as you drive through this low plateau, this westernmost edge, that's what you're going to see—basically horizontal rocks.

Now, what does that tell us about the Appalachians? That tells us that the energy came from east to west. It says the greatest amount of energy involved in the formation of the Appalachians was over there in that easternmost province in the Piedmont, and as you come to the west, the amount of energy is decreasing all the time. Now, they've noticed that for 150 years, but why? They never understood that. What was it about the creation of the Appalachians that results in this very systematic change in the fold attitudes as you go from east to west? They didn't know. Why? Plate tectonics hadn't come onto the scene yet. So, here's another reason why plate tectonics came onto the scene, why it gave us information we never had before. Now we understand how the Appalachians formed. How did it form? There was a big collision over there to the east, and that collision was a collision between two continental masses that resulted in the formation of Pangea. And now, we're back to Pangea again. We'll come back to this little structure of Appalachia because the other thing we want to talk about are, in fact, the faults.

Lecture Twenty-Nine
Faults and Joints

Scope:

In the study of any region, one of the basic questions to be answered is: Which way did the rock move? Once that is known, some interpretation can be made relative to the source of the forces and the direction of the maximum applied stress. In addition to the study of folds, such questions may be answered by observing the geometry of faults and joints. Faults, which are breaks along which there has been measurable movement, and joints, which are breaks along which there has been no measurable movement, comprise the two types of brittle deformation. Faults are of four basic types: *normal, thrust* or *reverse, strike-slip,* and *transform.* Of these, the best-known example is the San Andreas Fault in coastal California, which is a strike-slip fault. The most common of all geologic structures—joints—are of three types: *shear, tension,* and *columnar.*

Outline

I. A fault is a break in Earth's crust along which there has been measurable movement. Faults form by the application of both compressive and tensional forces.

    A. About 75% of faults form within a zone from Earth's surface to a depth of about 40 miles—the average thickness of Earth's crust. Only 20% of faults fall in the zone from 40 miles to 200 miles below the surface, and 5% from 200 miles to 450 miles below the surface. Below that, the rocks become totally plastic, and folds form, rather than faults. Faults are of four basic types: *normal, thrust* (with an angle less than 45° relative to the horizontal) or *reverse* (with an angle greater than 45° relative to the horizontal), *strike-slip,* and *transform.*

    B. The rock masses on opposite sides of normal or thrust faults are referred to as the *hanging wall* and the *footwall,* terms that were coined by miners who encountered faults while following beds of coal or mineral lodes.
        1. The footwall is the rock mass below a fault plane.
        2. The hanging wall is the rock mass above the fault plane.

C. Strike and dip are also used to describe the orientation of the fault plane.

    1. The strike of a fault plane is the direction of the line of intersection between the fault plane and the horizontal relative to the north geographic pole.

    2. The dip is the angle between the fault plane and the horizontal, plus the direction at which the fault plane slopes away perpendicular to the strike.

D. The *displacement* of a fault is the actual distance of movement along the fault plane.

    1. The vertical component of movement is called the *throw*.

    2. The horizontal component of movement is called the *heave*.

    3. If the throw is less than the heave, the result is a *low-angle fault*. If the reverse is true, the result is a *steep* or *high-angle fault*.

E. Normal faults form under tensional forces, with the hanging wall moving down relative to the footwall. The major sites of normal faulting are the divergent plate margins. The edges of continents are examples.

F. Normal faults also form in regions that have been subjected to uplift in response to tensional forces. For example, a massive crustal block rising 45 million years ago resulted in the formation of the Colorado Plateau and the Basin and Range Province.

    1. Apparently, the rocks of the Colorado Plateau were thick enough to resist deformation. As a result, they show little or no deformation, except for monoclinal folds and normal faulting along the plateau margin.

    2. Because the western portion of the crustal block, centered over Nevada, was thinner, tensional forces created many north-south–trending normal faults. Within this region, called the Basin and Range Province, normal faulting occurred in two scenarios. In the first, successive faults all dip in the same direction, resulting in a rotation of the block between faults and giving rise to a mountain range along one edge and a basin on the other. In the second scenario, faults alternate in dip direction, resulting in an up-thrown block called a *horst* that forms a mountain range and down-thrown block called a *graben* that forms a basin.

G. Most thrust or reverse faults form in response to non-rotational compressive forces and are characterized by the hanging wall having moved up relative to the footwall.

    1. Again, the difference between thrust and reverse faults is the angle of the fault plane, with thrust faults having an angle of less than $45°$ and reverse faults, greater than $45°$.

    2. A large-scale site of a thrust fault is a zone of subduction where one continental plate thrusts against another, for example, the west coast of South America. Here, the footwall has plunged beneath the hanging wall. Because the angle is greater than $45°$, the result is a reverse fault. The zone of subduction associated with the Andes Mountains is a reverse fault.

H. Where the zone of subduction is further offshore, the footwall dives beneath the hanging wall and the angle is shallower than $45°$, resulting in a thrust fault. When andesitic magma comes to the surface, an island arc is formed. The Japanese Islands are an example of this.

I. Strike-slip faults form from rotational compression, with the fault plane oriented vertically and parallel to the direction of applied force. The displacement of strike-slip faults is horizontal, with little or no vertical movement.

    1. Because the fault plane is vertical, the terms *hanging wall*, *footwall*, *heave*, and *throw* are not applicable.

    2. Strike-slip faults are described as either *right-lateral* or *left-lateral*, depending on the orientation of the forces and the relative movement of the rocks on opposite sides of the fault from the viewer.

    3. The best-known example of a right-lateral strike-slip fault in the United States is the San Andreas Fault.

J. Oceanic ridges are cut across by thousands of transform faults that allow the lithospheric plates to move on Earth's spherical surface.

    1. At first sight, transform faults appear to be strike-slip in character, and indeed, the central portion of the fault shifts in a strike-slip motion.

2. However, the fault also possesses two ends, along which the movement of the oceanic crust on opposite sides of the fault is in the same direction, albeit at different rates. At some point when the rates of movement on opposite sides of the fracture become equal, the fault terminates.

II. Joints are breaks in Earth's crust along which there has been little or no measurable movement. Of all geologic structures, joints are by far the most common, being found in all exposed rocks.

A. Perhaps the most common occurrence is in the layers of sedimentary rocks. Joints can be of three types: *shear*, *tension*, and *columnar*.

B. Shear joints form by the application of compressive forces and occur in sets that intersect at almost right angles. The direction of maximum compressive stress bisects the acute angle between sets of shear joints.

C. Tension joints also form from compressive forces. They form parallel to the direction of maximum compressive stress. They seem to be less abundant than shear joints.

D. Columnar jointing is a special type of fracture set that forms in igneous rock bodies. Hexagonal in cross-section, columnar joints are fractures that result as the basaltic magma cools and shrinks, forming a structure called a *devil's postpile*. The Palisades on the Hudson River's west bank provides an example; there, the formation is composed of a thick *sill*, a layer of solidified basaltic magma.

Recommended Reading:

Twiss, R. J., and E. M. Moores, *Structural Geology.*

Davis, G. H., and S. J. Reynolds, *Structural Geology of Rocks and Regions.*

Questions to Consider:

1. How can joints be used to determine the direction of maximum compressive stress?

2. How would one go about determining whether a strike-slip fault was right- or left-lateral?

Lecture Twenty-Nine—Transcript
Faults and Joints

Okay, on to the brittle fracture now. We're talking about faults and joints. Now, the difference between them, again, is actually pretty simple. A *fault*, by definition, is simply any break in the Earth's crust along which there has been measurable *movement*. It really doesn't say how much it has to move, just as long as you can measure it, it would be a fault. A *joint*, on the other hand, is a break in the Earth's crust along which there has been no appreciable or measurable movement.

Let's talk about faults first. And the question is, "Where would find the greatest concentration of faults?" And the answer would be, "Well, wherever you find the most brittle rocks." And the question is "Where would that be?" Well, I think you can see, now, just with what we've discussed so far, the most brittle rocks would be right at the surface of Earth, right at the surface of the crust—remember the crust is that outer layer. Like a crust on a pie, I think they gave the name *crust* to it because it was brittle. So, anyway, most of the faults in the world occur right at the surface. For example, we're going to talk about what has to be the most infamous fault in the United States, namely the San Andreas. You can go to California, and you can stand right on the San Andreas Fault. That would be a good example of a fault right at the surface, and that's where most of them are.

Now, as you go down into Earth, the number of faults drops off really, really fast because the rocks are becoming less and less brittle and more and more plastic. For example, once you get down to about 40 miles, the number of faults that occur within the surface at 40 miles of depth, about 75% of them—they're really dropping off fast—because once you go below that 40 miles, then you're starting to get in the plastic zone of deformation. Things are plastic, remember, they're flowing like liquids. Liquids don't break. So, if they don't break, they don't form faults. Once you go below about 40 miles, and that's what the significance of 40 miles is, if we think way back, now, to our early discussion, that's the average thickness of Earth's crust: 40 miles. So, once you go below that—from about 40 miles down to, roughly, maybe 200 to 250 miles—only 20% of all the faults occur within that zone, dropping off really fast. Once you go below 250 miles down to about roughly 450 miles, there are only about 5% of all the faults on Earth. And once you go below 450 miles there just aren't any. Why? Because the rocks then become totally plastic. Note what that says: That says that where the folds form is down there in that plastic zone. As you drive along the road and you see a fold, one of the things I want you to think of in your mind is that fold, although you see it at road level now, or at the surface of Earth—that's not where it formed. Where it formed was very deep within the Earth. How was it brought to the surface? By either a fault bringing it to the surface, or by simply eroding all the thousands and thousands of feet of rock above it.

So, anyway, back to the faults. Now, in terms of kinds of faults: There really are four kinds. The first kind is what we call a normal fault, and don't ask me what the abnormal fault is. I don't know why they call it normal, but they call it *normal fault*. And then you have the *thrust faults*—or *reverse faults*. Now, the only difference between these two faults, as we'll see, is simply the angle of the fault relative to the horizontal. If it's less than 45°, then we call that a thrust fault. If it's more than 45°, then it's a reverse fault. Then the next kind is what we call a *strike-slip fault*. Then the final one is a *transform fault*. The first three—the normal, the thrust or reverse, and the strike-slip fault—we've known about those for a long, long, long time. The transform fault, however, just came on to the scene with the coming of plate tectonics. We never knew about those before.

Okay, let's talk about some measurements that we take on faults now, so we can describe them. We refer to hanging wall and foot wall. Here's what I want you to imagine: A block of rock you're holding in front of you, and it has a crack in it or a fracture that is now going to become a fault. And that fracture, let's say, dips away toward your right hand. If you just pull them apart you've got two blocks now. One's called the *hanging wall*, and one's called the *foot wall*. Now, which one's which? I might add that the names hanging wall and foot wall were given to these two masses of rock by miners who were sort of mining along, and they were following, perhaps, a vein of gold, or even a bed of coal, and they ran into this fault zone, now. Now, they had to figure out which do you go—up or down—to find out where it is on the other side. So, they found out when the working along this fault surface, there was a massive rock above them, over their heads, and so they called that block the hanging wall. The hanging wall would be the one if you took the other one away, it would be hanging over your head. So I suspect that's sort of why they called it that way.

Now, the other one called the foot wall—well, they found out that the foot wall was the one where they could actually walk up the fault's surface. Again, it would be the one where if you took away the other one you could actually walk on the fault's surface with your feet. So, there's your hanging wall and foot wall. They're very, very descriptive, and we'll use those a lot in describing the different kinds of faults.

The other thing we do, of course, is the old *strike and dip*. This is a planar feature, so you know what strike is. It's simply the line of intersection between the fault plane or surface, and the horizontal. And again it's a direction, so you say north, or north 45 west, or north 45 east, whatever it happens to be. And again, there's a dip to it. In this case, in our little block, we had it dipping to your right hand. So you have to tell which direction it dips to, just like before. Of course, you could put the fracture the other way, you see—so in our little block, you're picturing this thing as dipping to your right hand. So, anyway, we have the strike and dip.

Then we have displacement. Now, *displacement* is the actual movement of the fault itself. Here's what I want you to visualize. Putting your hands together—palm to palm like that—and then moving, let's say, have your hands sort of dipping away to the left. That would be the fault zone. And what you're going to do now is you're going to simply move your left hand up relative to your right hand. I use my left hand because I'm a lefty; you can turn this way if you want to. But, anyway, your left hand is moved up to the right and so note, the distance between the fingertips of your right hand and the fingertips of your left hand—that's how far the fault actually moved. That's what displacement is all about. Displacement is the actual movement of the fault along the fault's surface. But note: You could do the same thing if you put your hands back again by simply lifting your left hand straight up, and then moving it over horizontally, and you're right back where you started again. So, in other words, you can sort of take that displacement and you can resolve it into two other measurements—a vertical one and a horizontal one. The vertical one is called the *throw*. The horizontal one is called the *heave*. So, we use those two terms, again, to describe folds if you want to use it that way—because, for example, if you had a 45° angle slope, then throw and heave would be equal to each other. If the throw was less than the heave, then you see it would be a low-angle fault. And if the heave was less than the throw, then you'd have a very steep fault like that. So, we can use those two.

Let's talk about kinds of faults now. Let's go on and talk about normal faults. So, back to our block again. We've got our block of rock. Picture now, the break, the fault zone is dipping away to your right hand. You're holding it in front of you. And we're going to subject this, now, to *tension*. Now, you can just imagine, now, what's going to happen. As you pull it apart, that hanging wall, the one that's in your right hand, is going to drop down relative to the foot wall—which is in your left hand, which is going to move up. It's a relative thing. What does that mean? Well, note: I could do the same thing by taking the hanging wall and moving it down, or the foot wall and moving it up. It's a relative motion between the two. But by definition, a fault with a hanging wall that has moved down relative to the foot wall—then that's what we call a normal fault.

Question: Where have we seen these before? Well, we've seen them a lot in our discussion so far. What I want you to do now is think all the way back to our early discussions of plate tectonics, and I want you to think about the *divergent plate margins*—where they're being pulled apart, you see, under tension. That's where normal faults form—under tension. So the first picture I would sort of bring back to your mind would be the rift zone. Remember you go down to Albuquerque, New Mexico, and here you have this rift zone going up into Colorado, and what you see there are these cracks that come to the surface of the ground. What those cracks are, that's the appearance at the surface of high-angled normal faults that are being created as a result of pulling the crust of Earth apart.

If we continue that on, remember, that developed into the rift valley, and remember the picture of the rift valley? Each side of the rift valley had these very high-angle faults. Those are normal faults. And the idea is the down-going block, basically the hanging wall, that's what forms the valley floor. So, as you pull this thing apart, the hanging wall's dropping down, and now we have a valley. Then you filled it with water, and then we had the linear ocean like the Red Sea. Now, we're going to break the Red Sea in the middle, which is actually happening as we speak, and finally we're going to pull the whole thing apart, and now we're going to have two continents moving away from each other. But here's the important part to realize. Think about the edge of those continents now. As those two continents are coming apart, what you're really doing is you're taking with each one its share of that original rift valley and its original share of those high-angle normal faults. So if you could see the continent in cross-section, then say that's bordering an opening ocean, the thing that characterizes the edge of the continent itself are these very large, high-angle, normal faults—still moving as we speak because there are still tensional forces on this entire system as the ocean continues to open. I want you to sort of remember that because we're going to come back to that breaking down and the normal faults along the edge of the continent a little bit later. So, anyway, that would be probably the best place I could think of for normal faults.

The other one I might just mention: We talked an awful lot, too, about the Basin and Range Province—remember, out in Nevada? If you went up to Nevada, here you would have these long, parallel mountain ranges and long, parallel valleys. Here's another classic example of tensional faults. Remember picking up the entire Colorado Plateau, that whole area? If you pick something up like that—although we're talking here about vertical uplift, the forces that are in play within that massive rock are tensional. Just think, for example, of putting your hands under one of those big layer cakes you buy for parties and trying to pick it up. It just falls to pieces like that. They pull away. Those are tensional forces. It's exactly the same thing. Over there in the Basin and Range—rather than on the Colorado Plateau, there was no faulting—but over there on that Basin and Range, all these high-angled, normal faults occurred. The reason why, we think, is the rocks are thinner over there, weaker than they were over here in the Colorado Plateau. So, as a result, we have these high-angled, normal faults—and, in some cases, all the faults dip in the same direction.

If you can picture this now: Two faults, normal faults, dipping in the same direction, and picture what happens to the rock between them. It sort of rotates, doesn't it? Because—let's say they're all dipping to your right. The right hand, for example, represents one fault; your left hand represents the other one. But just picture, now, basically to the right of the right hand, that's the down-going fault block. So, here is this foot wall sticking up in the air now. And if you think of the same thing over here on your left hand, in between, the down-going block is forming a valley between these two ridges. So, you have mountain ranges in the Basin and Range that are consisting of mountain ranges where one side of the mountain range is a fault scarp, and the others simply are sedimentary rocks dipping down against the next fault scarp. The other scenario there is where they alternate in direction. You'll have faults that will go in one direction—let's say, east then west, and then east, then west. And if you picture that little model, what happens, then, is you have what they call *horst*, which is an up-thrown block—that would be basically the foot wall block. And then the down-thrown block would be what they call *graben*. So you have the horst and graben structure. That would be another—sort of a localized—example of tensional faults and normal faulting. So, anyway, normal faults.

Now let's talk about reverse faults or thrust faults. Remember, the big difference between these two, now, is simply going to be the angle of faulting. If, for example, the fault is actually less than 45°, then it's going to be a thrust fault, and if it is more than 45°, we're going to call it a reverse fault. The fact of the matter is most geologists when they're out describing faults use one term or the other interchangeably, but there is a difference between it technically anyway.

So, basically, here's the deal now. Let's say we're going to form these things. How do we form them? We're going to form them under non-rotational compression. If you think of non-rotational compression—think again of your block of rock, sitting in front of you, and the fault plane, again, dips toward your right hand. Now we're going to put this thing under non-rotational compression. We're going to force it together. Again, you can just imagine now what's going to happen. Here's the hanging wall, remember, in your right hand. The foot wall's in your left hand. As you push them together, the right-hand block, the hanging wall, is going to ride up—relative to the foot wall, which rides down. Note: That's directly the opposite of the normal fault. Why? It's directly the opposite of the forces. Rather than tensional forces now, we've got compressional forces—so the result is completely opposite. So, now we have the scenario where the hanging wall has moved up—relative to the foot wall, and, by definition now, that becomes either a reverse fault or a thrust fault, depending upon what that angle is.

Again, now, knowing what you know about geology—and we've talked a lot about basic structures now—where would you expect to find large-scale thrust faulting, large-scale either thrust or reverse faulting, compressional faulting? If you think about that: Where is the zone where you have the greatest amount of compressional forces, rocks coming together like that? Well, you've got to think of the zone of subduction. You've got to think of those convergent margins because that's the biggest head-on collision in the world. You can't get any bigger collision than one continental plate ramming into another continental plate. So if you look at the zones of subduction, let's take a look at them. Let's take the example of the one off the west coast of South America. Remember the big deal about that one is: The zone of subduction is just sort of right offshore a little bit, not very many miles: maybe a few miles or tens of miles. Here's the picture now: You're going to put those plates together fingertip to fingertip now. What you're going to do, your right hand, again, is the hanging wall; the left hand is the foot wall. What's going to happen is the rocks are going to break—remember the down-bowing of the ocean for the deep sea trench—and then finally it's going to break, and that oceanic plate is going to dive down underneath the continent. Note, hanging wall has moved up relative to the foot wall.

But which one is doing the plunging? The foot wall is doing the plunging in this case. The hanging wall, more or less, is just sitting there. That's the continental plate you see. So, in this case, that foot wall is doing the plunging, and that's your zone of subduction. Now, being close to the continent like that, the angle is greater than 45°, and so this would technically be described as a reverse fault. What happens? Once it gets down there deeply enough, you start melting rocks. And you have, of course, the granitic magma that's going to come up and emplace themselves in the edge of the continent. But the other magma, remember, is andesitic. It breaks through to the surface and generates that on-land continental arc volcanoes, like the Andes Mountains. So, that would be a perfect example of a reverse fault—in this case, interestingly enough, the foot wall diving beneath the hanging wall.

Well, let's go to the other scenario. The other scenario, now, was where that zone of subduction was a little bit further offshore—maybe quite a bit, maybe 100 miles, maybe 200 miles. Then, what you have is the same thing again: Your right hand now, once again, is the hanging wall; the left hand, once again, is the potential foot wall. But now, the break occurs, the ocean bottom dives down, what you're doing is you're generating that deep-sea trench, and then that finally breaks. Once again now, the foot wall starts to dive beneath the hanging wall, but now the angle is much shallower. Now the angle is so shallow, we would have to call that a thrust fault because it's usually less than 45°. Now, you see, it's further offshore, maybe 100 miles offshore, maybe 200 miles. As that thing goes down, it's going to take it awhile to get down there to heat up, but then the molten rock forms in the same way as before. You're generating these granitic magmas and these andesitic magmas. But in this case, when the andesitic magma comes to the surface, it's the ocean bottom. And as a result, you build this island arc scenario, where you have these series of volcanic islands made of andesitic magmas now called *lavas*, of course—and you're talking about things like the Aleutian Islands and the Japanese Islands. Note: The difference is, it's simply a question of the angle at which that diving takes places. But note: In both cases, now, we're dealing with the foot wall diving beneath the hanging wall. Anyway, that would be the biggest example I can give, but there are many, many, many other examples of thrust faulting and reverse faulting around the world. I think we'll hold a little bit until we get to the Appalachians because there are a couple there I'd really like to show you.

Let's see the next one, strike-slip faults. Now, we have to sort of visualize this looking down now. We're looking down from above. So here's your hands—put your hands together—and we're looking down at the Earth, looking at the backs of your hands, and so right hand, left hand. The deal is that strike-slip faults form as a result of rotational compression. Rotational. So what you're going to do with your hands, let's say, well, one possibility is the left hand moves up relative to the right hand. That would be a rotational compression. Or the right hand moves up relative to the left hand. That would be rotational compression. Here's the deal: Whenever you form a fault as the result of those horizontally delivered rotational compressions, the fault always forms, of course, between those two moving blocks vertically. So that's the characteristic of strike-slip faults: They're vertical faults. And note: In this case, there's no hanging wall or foot wall because there's no vertical movement. It's all horizontal movement we're talking about.

So, here's the picture. Let's say we take the first picture. The left hand moves out in front of the right hand. That's scenario one. The other one, scenario two: You just change the relative directions of the movement around, so now, the right hand moves out in front of the left hand. How do we tell those apart? They're totally different, of course, but how do you tell them apart? Let's say, for example, we take the first scenario where the left hand moves out in front of the right hand. Well, let's say, there was a roadway that was coming along here before the faulting occurred, and the road was split in half—so we have one half on the left hand, one half on the right hand. Your picture, now, is the left hand up in front of the right hand. You're walking down the road. You're walking toward the fault, and you finally get to the fault. Question: Which way do you have to turn to pick up the road on the other side? If you just think about it, you're coming down this road, and you'd have to turn to the right to pick up the road on the other side. Note: It makes no difference if you're coming down this road. Whichever way you're coming toward the fault, whichever side you're on, you still have to turn to the right. So that scenario we just described with your left hand out in front of your right, that would form a *right-lateral strike-slip fault*, and that's how we describe it. Note if we just did the other scenario—your right hand is out in front of the left hand—now, what we have is a *left-lateral*. Because, again, think about coming down that road and running into that fault, which way do you have to turn to pick it up on the other side? In either case, you'd have to turn to the left. So you have right-lateral or left-lateral strike-slip faults.

Now, let me give you the example—probably the very, very best one I could think of—it's our old favorite, the San Andreas Fault. We're going to talk about the San Andreas Fault a lot more when we get around to earthquakes in a lecture to come. But it turns out that the San Andreas Fault, basically, is a right-lateral strike-slip fault. Note: Right off the bat—now, I'm sort of giving little secrets away from that lecture, but I think it's okay—is California slipping off into the ocean? You hear that a lot, "California is going to slip off into the ocean." No, no, it'll never slip off into the ocean because there's no vertical component, you see. It's not an up and down thing; it's a side-by-side thing. What's happening is that portion of California, the part that has Los Angeles and San Diego on it, is moving northward relative to the rest of the continent. And someday Los Angeles will be a suburb of San Francisco, but we'll get to that one. That would be a really, really good example—the best one I can think of—of a strike-slip fault.

Now, the transform faults. We never knew about these until plate tectonics came on to the scene. Here's the deal with the transform faults. Remember those oceanic ridges we talked about a lot: And here we have every ocean has one; they all interconnect with each other, we're talking 40,000 miles, the most dominant feature on Earth's surface take away the water, that would be the first thing you see coming in from space. We always talk about these oceanic ridges as though they were long, continuous mountain ranges. Well, they aren't really. If you look at an artist's rendition of what they think the ocean bottom looks like, what you'll find out is that these oceanic ridges are cut across by hundreds, and hundreds, and hundreds of cross faults—we call them *transform faults.*

Here's the deal. If you just sort of put your fingers together and sort of imagine, now, that's the ridge. And just move—let's say, your right hand is above your left—and you simply move your left hand over: Now, you see there's an offset between the finger on your right hand and the finger on your left hand. That would be a transform fault. Now, think about the movement between the ends of the ridge. Well, it looks to me like your talking here about a strike-slip movement. Well, it *is* a strike-slip movement. In other words, the rocks on either side are going in opposite directions. It is a strike-slip movement—then why don't we call it a *strike-slip fault.* I guess we could, except for the ends. The ends go beyond the ridges, and so out there on both sides, you have a fault where the rocks on opposite sides are going in the same direction now. Now, different velocities or speeds—that's the reason why they're broken apart. The fault will exist as long as they're going in the same direction at a different speed. But sooner or later, they're going in the same direction at the same speed, and the fault comes to an end. So that's what your transform faults are.

Why do you have them? The reason why you have them, picture now, the movement of the plates. The plates aren't moving on a flat surface, even though what the Flat Earth Society says it is, it really isn't. It is really a sphere. The point is: Here you have these plates actually moving across the spherical surface. In order to allow them to do that, cup your hands together with your fingers and, let's say, represent the North Pole and down here—at the bottom of your hands—that represents the equator. You see, to make the plates move, the closer you get to the equator, the faster they have to go. In order to allow those plates to move on a curved surface like that or a spherical surface, that's the reason why you have these transform faults. So, anyway, so there are the four different kinds of faults.

And now, on to the joints—breaks along which there is little or no movement. I say "little," but there always could be some, I guess. Someone always asks me, "How about a little teeny bit?" Okay, fair enough: "no appreciable movement." The three kinds of joints are *tension, sheer,* and *columnar* joints. We're going to hold off on the columnar joints until last because they are a little bit different. So, let's just talk about the sheer joints and the tension joints. And to do this let's go back to our discussion of karst topography. Let's go back to our discussion of solution sinkholes. What you have— remember we took all the regolith away from this layer of limestone, and the layer of limestone, remember, was cut, broken, by these cross joints that intersect each other at right angles? Well, not quite. In the sheer set, the so-called sheer joints, there are two sets of joints. The one set everybody's parallel to one direction, and then there's another one almost at right angles to that. I say, "almost" because where they intersect there's an obtuse and an acute angle between them. Now, when I say acute, we're talking here maybe 85°, so it's almost at right angles. Here's the deal: If you were to think about taking, now, a layer of rock, brittle layer; and you're going to compress it now, under non-rotational compression; you're going to exceed the elastic limit just by a little bit—all you have to do is just a little bit more surface area, remember that; and it cracks. That's what the joints are.

The sheer joints are these sets of almost-intersecting-at-right-angle joints. Now, here's the secret of them. That acute angle—if you were to bisect that acute angle, that's the direction from which the forces came. So other than forming the solution sinkholes, the other important thing about these sheer joints is we can use them to tell from which direction the forces were coming. Well, at least one of two: You don't know whether it was coming from the right or the left, perhaps. But note: Somewhere else there has to be some other information that allows you to choose that option, too. But that's what that is. Those are your sheer joints.

Now, in addition to that, you've got tension joints. Now, the best way to picture this one. Picture taking a deck of cards on end, standing them up on end, and squeezing them. Now, that's non-rotational compression, right? But the cards pop open—that's tensional forces: that's what actually pulled one card away from the other, so that would be the so-called *tension joint*. Note: The tension joints follow parallel to the forces that are applied to the rock. My experience is the sheer joints seem to be more abundant. Now, someone else may have a different experience, but all the ones I've measured—almost all of them are the sheer type.

Now, the last one, columnar jointing. This is a very, very special thing. You hear about devil's post piles everywhere you go. Every country has a devils post pile. These things typically form—usually, not always now, but usually—where you're dealing with layers of solidified basaltic magmas because they're formed underground. So picture now, this layer of basalt—never got to the surface—it's in a crack, and it's now cooling off. It's a magma—a basaltic magma, now—cooling off. The surface cools on both sides, and when things cool they contract. Now, think about points of contraction on this surface. If it was uniform in all directions, what the crack would form would be a circle. You'd have these circular cracks, and the problem is just think about drawing circles and intersecting on a tabletop. There's going to be a space between them, you see. Mother Nature doesn't like spaces between things. She likes everything to be filled in. So here's the deal. When this shrinkage takes place on both sides, it actually doesn't form a circular crack: It forms a hexagonal crack. The secret of the hexagon, it's the geometric figure that most closely approximates a circle, and yet when put side-by-side will completely fill the area. Think of your bathroom floor, that's why you have those hexagonal tiles on your bathroom floor. Almost a circle, it satisfies that almost uniform attraction. So, if you have a hexagonal crack on one side, there's one on the other side, and they're heading toward each other. Eventually they'll run together, and what you'll end up with is columnar jointing—so that's what that is. They form pillars or posts—the Devil's Post Pile. Another good example of columnar jointing that a lot of people have seen would be the Palisades over there on the western bank of the Hudson

River. The Palisades they're talking about, a *palisade* is a column, you see. So, that is the edge of a fairly thick *sill*, we call that: a layer of solidified basaltic magma forming these columnar joints.

So, anyway, there's our fractures, and the next topic we're going to go on to is going to take us into a very exciting topic—we're going to continue our discussion of fracturing and faulting, and the topic is going to be earthquakes.

Lecture Thirty
Earthquakes

Scope:

Earthquakes are associated with convergent plate margins—with a high degree of severity—and divergent plate margins—with a lesser degree of severity. *Seismic shock waves*, which reflect the amount of energy released during faulting, are of two types: *shear waves*, which are transmitted through solids, and *compression waves*, which are transmitted through solids, liquids, or gases. The *focus* and *epicenter* of the earthquake must be calculated to locate the origin of the earthquake. The shock waves emanating from the focus are categorized as *body waves*, while those emanating from the epicenter are categorized as *surface waves*. The latter are responsible for the visible damage caused by earthquakes.

Outline

I. For centuries, earth scientists have known where the major earthquakes occurred. They also knew they occurred in the same locales as the most violent volcanoes—the Ring of Fire in the Pacific Ocean basin, the Mediterranean-Himalayan zone, and the Indonesian zone.

   A. It was believed that one phenomenon was the cause of the other.

   B. With the advent of the theory of plate tectonics, we know that it is not a question of cause and effect; both volcanoes and earthquakes result from the activity of convergent plate or divergent plate margins, with convergent plate margins producing the most violent eruptions.

   C. The volcanism that occurs along zones of subduction is extremely violent, whereas the volcanism at oceanic ridges, for example, Iceland, is in the non-explosive Hawaiian phase.

      1. The difference lies in the difference between magmas. Andesitic magma coming to the surface in the zone of subduction is full of gas and is always explosive.

2. Basaltic magma, erupting at an oceanic ridge, on the other hand, brings very little gas to the surface and erupts with low intensity.

II. In order to explain why earthquakes associated with convergent plate margins are of much higher magnitude than those associated with divergent plate margins, we must review our discussion of stress and strain.

A. Under compression, rocks are very strong, whereas under tension, rocks are weak.

B. The many columns that characterize ancient Greek architecture indicate that the Greeks did not understand how to overcome the inherent weakness of rocks under tension. The ancient Romans invented the arch, the secret of which is the keystone at the top. Because the keystone acts as a wedge, the contact between the keystone and the adjacent component of the arch is under non-rotational compression, which is transferred throughout the structure. The arch works because rock is strongest under non-rotational compression.

C. The amount of energy stored before reaching the elastic limit is determined by the inherent strength of the rock.

1. Because rocks are very strong under compression, the amount of energy stored during the elastic phase of deformation and released during brittle failure will be potentially large. Conversely, rocks are inherently weak under tension, meaning that little energy is stored during the elastic phase of deformation and released during brittle failure.

2. Convergent plate margins at zones of subduction are subject to enormous compressive forces. Thus, earthquakes associated with these areas are of potentially high magnitude.

3. Earthquakes associated with divergent margins at rift zones, rift valleys, and oceanic ridges are the result of tensional forces and are always of low magnitude.

III. The energy released during faulting is in the form of shock waves, referred to specifically as *seismic shock waves*. In general, shock waves are of two types: *shear waves* and *compression waves*.

A. Shear waves can be transmitted only through solids; consider that only solids can be "sheared." The particles in a solid material through which the shock wave is propagated are moved perpendicular to the direction of propagation.

B. Compression waves can propagate through solids, liquids, or gases. As compression waves propagate, they move the materials back and forth in the direction of propagation.

    1. The best model to illustrate a compression wave is the toy spring called a Slinky.

    2. Our ears respond to compression waves that our brains interpret as sound.

IV. Two important points are used to locate the origin of earthquake energy: *focus* and *epicenter*.

A. The focus of an earthquake is the point at which the energy is released.

B. The epicenter of an earthquake is the point on Earth's surface immediately above the focus.

C. For earthquakes occurring at Earth's surface, the focus and epicenter are the same point.

D. Because faulting is a brittle response, most earthquake foci are located at Earth's surface, where the rocks are most brittle. The number of earthquake foci decrease in frequency with depth. The foci of earthquakes are categorized as *shallow, intermediate,* and *deep*.

    1. Shallow-focus earthquakes occur from Earth's surface to a depth of about 40 miles. Seventy-five percent of all earthquakes are shallow focus.

    2. Intermediate-focus earthquakes occur from a depth of 40 miles to about 200 miles. The frequency of intermediate-focus earthquakes drops to about 20%.

    3. Deep-focus earthquakes occur down to depths of about 400 miles. Earthquakes do not occur below this depth because the rocks become totally plastic.

V. Earthquake shock waves are categorized as *body waves* and *surface waves*.

A. Body waves originate at the focus and are propagated through Earth's interior.

1. Body waves are both shear and compression in type, with both types of wave following the exact same path. The shear body waves are designated *s-waves*. The compression body waves are designated *p-waves*.

2. Body waves are very low amplitude and very high velocity. The materials through which they pass experience a very small amount of movement. The body waves pass through Earth at a velocity of 24,000 mph.

B. Because the epicenter is the point closest to the point of energy release, the epicenter is the point on Earth's surface where the energy is at a maximum.

C. Surface waves originate and spread out from the epicenter. In contrast to body waves, the amplitudes of surface waves can be high enough to be seen as they propagate across Earth's surface but travel at much lower velocities.

1. Surface waves are of two types: *Love waves* and *Rayleigh waves*.

2. Love waves are shear waves and consist of the horizontal portion of shear, moving Earth's surface back and forth horizontally and perpendicular to the direction of propagation.

3. Rayleigh waves are a combination of the vertical component of shear plus the to-and-fro motion of compression, resulting in a rolling motion as they move across Earth's surface.

4. Surface waves are responsible for most of the damage resulting from an earthquake, with Love waves being more destructive than Rayleigh waves.

Recommended Reading:

Hough, S. E., *Earthquake Science: What We Know (and Don't Know) about Earthquakes.*

Questions to Consider:

1. What is the source of the energy released in the form of an earthquake shock wave?

2. Why are the earthquakes associated with convergent plate margins always of greater magnitude than those associated with divergent plate margins?

Lecture Thirty—Transcript
Earthquakes

Earthquakes and volcanic activity have to be the most exciting phases of geology, at least in my opinion. And the interesting thing about these two phenomena is that if you sort of go back in time, there's always been a relationship between the two that has been known for a very, very, very long time. For example, if we went back even before the days before geology—remember, geology didn't come on to the scene until what, the mid-1700s. I mean, there were Earth scientists before that who had an idea of what the world was like because by this time we're already sailing around the world and exploring distant places.

So, these people already knew, for example, where most of the volcanism was and also where the major, killer earthquakes were. And they seemed to be all associated with the same kinds of places. For example, they knew—even then—that most of the volcanic activity—the killer volcanoes, certainly, and the killer earthquakes—were located in a zone around the Pacific Ocean. That forever has been referred to as the *Ring of Fire*, and even today, that's where most of your volcanic activity is. Most of the active volcanoes at any one time are located around the Pacific Ocean basin. If you just keep track of where all the potential killer earthquakes are over a period of time, you'll find out that is also a zone of very high incidence of potential killer earthquakes. They knew about that one.

Then they knew where there was another one, and the other one went through the Mediterranean, sort of heading over toward the Himalaya: And that's the zone, of course, of volcanic activity: Mount Vesuvius, Mount Etna, and a number of others. It's also a zone of potential killer earthquakes. We just had a number of them over in Pakistan and places like that. That's part of this zone we're talking about. So they knew about that one, and they also knew about the other one. The other one went down through Indonesia and eventually ended up over the west margin of the Pacific—sort of the Pacific Rim kind of thing seemed to tie together with this one. Today, as a matter of fact, there's a volcanic eruption going on that is the result of eruptions in Indonesia. These are also places of extreme volcanic activity and earthquake activity. For example, the earthquake that caused the huge wave—we call it *tsunami*—that had wreaked destruction on Sri Lanka—that was in the Indonesian zone. So they've known about these for a long, long, long, long time.

But remember, this was before the days of plate tectonics. They didn't know why they were associated, but the fact that they were. This led geologists for many, many moons—I'm not sure I could say right up to the time I took geology my first time—but for many, many moons, this was the reason why they thought one was the cause of the other, because they had this same pattern worldwide. And there were people who argued that a volcanic eruption causes an earthquake to occur. Their argument was as the molten rock forces its way to the surface, pushing rocks out of the way, cracking them, breaking them, an earthquake occurs. There are other people who said, "No, that's not the way it works. The way it works is you have this earthquake that breaks things up and allows the molten rock to come to the surface." They went back and forth, back and forth. It turns out, of course, that it isn't a question of cause and effect. The reason why they're associated with each other is because they're both associated with the same thing: zones of subduction. You see, we never knew that until plate tectonics came onto the scene.

Once plate tectonics came onto the scene, then we had another zone we didn't know about before. We had another zone of active volcanism—which we call, of course, the *oceanic ridge* (now, of course, the rifts, too, but the main one is the oceanic ridge). And once we discovered the oceanic ridge, we also discovered it was highly volcanic active. I mean, molten rock was coming to the surface along the summit of the mid-oceanic ridges and creating new oceanic crusts, we've talked a lot about that. But the interesting thing is if you compare that volcanism to the volcanism that occurs along the zones of subduction, that was different. Remember the volcanism that occurred along the zones of subduction: Those were all potential killers; those eruptions never occurred non-explosively. So, that's where your potential killer volcanic eruptions were. Whereas along the oceanic ridges—a good example, of course, being Iceland—you never had that. It was the Hawaiian phase—remember that? Well now, we understand that one, too. It was simply a question of the different kinds of magmas. In one case, you were dealing with an andesitic magma coming to the surface in association with the zone of subduction—lots of gas, always going to be explosive eruptions, so there's your potential killers. But over in the other case, now, here comes this basaltic magma to the surface, with very little gas by the

©2006 The Teaching Company Limited Partnership

time it gets there, so you never have an explosive eruption—again, on Iceland, which would be a typical example of an oceanic ridge.

Well, we understand that one. But here's the other one we have to figure out. What we don't know yet, at this time before plate tectonics: Why is it, now, that the earthquakes that are associated with the oceanic ridges are very low in intensity? And they are. We're going to talk about Richter Scale stuff next name. But these are all very, very low on the Richter Scale. We're talking about earthquakes—you might be able to feel them, but no one was ever killed by an earthquake along an oceanic ridge—we're talking, let's say, Iceland for example. No one was ever killed by an earthquake up there. And why? Why is it that the earthquakes that are associated with the zones of subduction are always potential killers anyway, and those that are associated with the oceanic ridges are not?

Well, I think all you have to do, now, is think about the difference between those two zones. For the zone of subduction, we're talking here compressive forces. We're talking about the biggest compressive forces on Earth. You can't get any bigger head-on collision than a zone of subduction. On the other hand, on the oceanic ridge, we're talking about tensional forces. You're talking about pulling rocks apart. Does that have something to do with it? Yes, it does as a matter of fact. Here's all you have to remember: Under compression, rocks are very, very, very strong—very strong under compression; very, very, weak under tension. For example, you can take a slab of rock and put it down, and you can stack as many rocks on top of it as you want. Picture the highest building you know: big tower, whatever—I don't care how high you build it—the rock on the bottom will withstand the weight of everything you put above. Why? That's non-rotational compression we're talking. That's where rocks are really, really, really strong. On the other hand, you take that same rock, and you chuck it up in some kind of a vice thing and try to pull it apart, we're talking tensional forces now, it's the same rock, but it will break very, very quickly. Why? Rocks under tension are very, very weak.

Well, let me give you a little trivia—I love trivia, of course, and especially historical trivia, so here's a little bit of historic trivia for you that sort of hopefully will allow you to remember that thing about rocks being strong under compression, weak under tension. What I want you to do is to imagine the difference, now, between the architecture of Ancient Greece and the architecture of Rome. Okay, all right, architecture of Ancient Greece: We're talking, now, the Acropolis. Up on top of the hill behind Athens you have the Parthenon. And what is it that characterizes the Parthenon and everything else they built for that matter? Lots, and lots, and lots of columns. They loved those columns. Did you ever wonder why they did that? Just think of how much that must have cost to make all those columns—be great for the column makers, of course. But why did they do that?

Well, I think the reason why the Greeks did that is because they never could figure out how to overcome the inherent weakness of rocks under tension. For example, here's what they did: You have a column, and then they spanned between the columns with a flat layer of rock they called a *lintel*. Picture this flat layer of rock now—note the forces. The forces are rotational compression. The up forces will be the columns underneath the ends of the lintel. The weight of the lintel itself—and everything you put above it, of course—is pushing down on the lintel: So note, you have rotational compression. So, the lintel, now, is being subjected to rotational compression. But if you subject something like that to rotational compression, the forces inside are going to be tensional. Rocks are very, very weak under tension. So the problem was that whenever they built these buildings, they found there was a limit as to how far they could get the posts apart. For example, I'm sure that when they built the Parthenon, they would have been very happy to put a post at each corner and put the roof on. But they couldn't do that. Because they found out that as you took the posts further and further apart—and as that lintel got longer, and longer, and longer—pretty soon, it would fail even under its own weight—let alone whatever you put above—and it fails by tensional forces: very, very weak.

Here's just a little experiment that you can do by yourself if you want to prove it. If you take a pencil, for example, and you just hook it between your fingers like that, the two hands, and take your thumbs and push down on it. This, the force I'm adding now, this is rotational compression: up on the ends, down in the middle, rotational compression. But what's forming inside the pencil, in this case, are tensional forces. So, if you do it long enough, the pencil will break, and the points come away from each other. Why did they come away? Because there were tensional forces being developed within it. They never could figure out how to overcome those tensional forces. So, as a result, when they built their buildings they had lots, and lots, and lots of columns, which you must admit really looks good. I mean, what would the Parthenon look like with four posts? That could be something different, again. Okay, so much for the Greeks.

Now let's go to the Romans. What characterizes Roman architecture? Well, it's the Roman arch. The Roman arch is what characterizes Roman architecture. And the interesting thing about the Romans—you know they've been given credit for an awful lot of stuff that they really didn't do. What the Romans were really good at was going into some place, sort of taking it over. They were good administrators. But then they would take whatever these other people had and maybe embellish it a little bit, maybe pass it off as their own—but it really wasn't theirs, and everybody knew it. But what they did do, they did do some things: For example they invented concrete. And I think that's one of the reasons why the Romans were such good builders. They finally invented a way to stick rocks together, you see. That's pretty important if you want to build a big building like the Colosseum. So, anyway, they invented the arch, and the secret of the arch is that keystone.

The keystone at the top—remember what it is? It's a wedge-shaped rock like that. Here's what wedges do: What wedges do if you load them from above, they force the forces out to the sides. I don't care whether it's a keystone in an arch or a chisel. They all work the same way: They direct the forces away from the keystone or the chisel. So, here's the point. If you load an arch from above, the keystone throws the forces out to the side, so the contact between the keystone and the first block of the arch, that's non-rotational compression. Then the contact between that block and the next block, that's non-rotational compression. And for the next one, the same thing. Finally, we're down to the top of the post, that's non-rotational compression. And, of course, the contact with the post or the column and the ground, that's non-rotational compression. So note: In the entire arch from one side to the other, the only forces there are: non-rotational compression. Rocks are very, very strong under non-rotational compression. So there's the reason why—I don't think there's any limit to how big of an arch you can build. But you can thank the Romans, then, for all the beautiful arch ceilings and dome ceilings around the world—and anything that's an arch. I'm thinking of the bridge across the New River Gorge in West Virginia. This thing is huge, but yet it's very, very strong because it's an arch. Any arch is strong like that because loaded from above, the forces within it are basically non-rotational compression. It was the Romans that figured that one out. Okay, so much for that.

Now, well, what's the big deal then? What does it mean to be strong and weak? Rocks are strong under compression—and weak under tension. Okay. What does it really, really mean though? Well, let's go back to our discussion, now, of deformation of things and stuff. Elastic phase, brittle phase, okay. During the elastic phase, you're going to store energy, and you're going to store it up to the elastic limit. At that point, something's going to break, okay? So let's say something is strong. What does "strong" really mean? Well, what "strong" really means, this rock we're talking about, you can start applying any kind of force to it, and it will start absorbing the energy and storing the energy up to its elastic limit. But being strong means that the elastic limit, now, is going to be very, very high. What does that mean? Well, that means during the elastic phase of deformation you're going to store a lot of energy in this rock during that phase. So, finally, when you finally reach the elastic limit and you go beyond and it breaks, if you stored a lot of energy, then you release a lot of energy. On the other hand, if something is weak that means you reach the elastic limit pretty fast; you don't store very much energy before you get there; and when the stuff breaks—the same rock, perhaps under tension now—you didn't store much in the elastic phase, which means you're not going to get very much back after the elastic limit is reached.

Here's the picture, then. We're talking about zones of subduction, for example. We're talking compressive forces of the first order. No place on Earth are you going to have those kind of compressive forces: Enormous amounts of energy can be stored during that collision between those two plates. When it finally breaks and forms those thrust faults or reverse faults in what we call the *zone of subduction*, you've already stored enormous amounts of energy. That energy is released, and—as a result—you have a potential killer earthquake.

Any time that you have an earthquake, you hear about it on TV, or you read about it in the paper, here's all I'd like you to do: Whip out a map of the place. Remember not many of these places, but whip out your map, and look to see where the earthquake was, and I will absolutely guarantee you it will be along one of those zones of subduction. The earthquakes we just mentioned, the one in Indonesia, the one in Pakistan: Those are all zones of subduction we're talking about. That's the reason why we're talking compressive forces here, storing an awful lot of energy during that compressive phase.

How about the oceanic ridge or any other rift for that matter? We're talking about pulling the rocks apart. Under tension like that, the rocks are really not very strong at all: They're really pretty weak. So as we pull this rock apart, now, we're storing energy during the elastic phase—remember, the elastic phase is always first—and we're storing energy up until the elastic limit. But remember what it means to be weak: Under tension, it means that you're going to reach that elastic limit pretty quick. And when you reach the elastic limit pretty quick, you haven't stored much energy—so, as a result, there's not much energy to be released. So, as a result, any earthquake that's associated with a divergent margin—we're talking any of the rift zones, rift valleys, and, of course, the big one, the oceanic ridge—we're talking about an earthquake where you're talking maybe 2 or 3 on the Richter Scale—which, when we get to that, you can just barely feel that. So, in other words, there's the reason why now. We now understand why the earthquakes with those two zones are totally different. It's simply the response of materials to stress is all it is. You've already learned all about that.

Let's talk about shock waves now. The energy that's released whenever rocks break, they release shock waves. A *shock wave* is a general term. If it happens to be generated as a result of the movement of a fault—in other words, an earthquake—we call it a seismic wave. A *seismic wave* is simply a shock wave strictly associated, now, with a fault movement. There are two fundamentally different kinds of shock waves. One's called *shear*. Now, picture this, now, in a shear wave—let's say the shear wave was traveling away from you—so that's the *direction of propagation* now—traveling away from you. What it's doing, whatever it's moving through now, it's moving that material perpendicular to the direction of propagation. For example, the little drawing shows it moving back and forth horizontally, and up and down vertically— but remember now, perpendicular is perpendicular. Those are simply two perpendicular directions, but in between those there's a whole mess of other ones. So, the idea is that as the shock wave goes through, what's happening to the rock or whatever it's going through is going out and in, and out and in like that, moving the stuff perpendicular—that's the important part. So that's the shear wave.

Now the compression wave is kind of totally different. In the *compression wave*, if you can imagine the shock wave moving away from you again, the material it's moving through is moving the stuff back and forth in the direction in which it's going. In other words, it's a back and forth kind of thing. The best sort of model I've ever seen for that (if you want to sort of picture it) is the old Slinky—you know, that spring. You take a Slinky, and you put most of the coil in one hand and a few in the other, and you let it go, and it goes BOING! BOING! BOING!—back and forth like that: Well, that would be a typical compressive wave.

Here's a sort of little tidbit of trivia, a sideline. The shear waves: The shear waves will only go through solids. Why? Only solids can be sheared or cut, you see. For example, let's say, you take a pair of shears, and if you snap them around in the air, really not doing anything, see. And if you put them in a bucket of water and snap them around, well, you're not really doing anything either because you're just making a mess. But if you snap them around and put your finger in there, you cut your finger off. Why? They only go through solids. They don't go through liquids and gasses.

On the other hand, compressive waves can go through anything: solids, liquids, or gasses. For example, you're hearing my voice. That means my voice—the shock wave that is being made by my throat, here, is traveling across the air to your ear. So, it can go through air or gas. On the other hand, you can hear underwater. Well, that's because these compressive waves can go through liquid, too. Or you can put your ear to a railroad track if you want to and listen for the train coming, because it goes through solids. So, compressive waves can go through any medium whatsoever— whereas the shear waves can only go through solids. So much for the kind of shock waves now.

Now on to two words: *focus* and *epicenter*. Now, these are two words that oftentimes people use synonymously, but they're totally different. So, let's picture this now: A big hunk of the Earth's crust, a big cube, and now I have on the cube—picture the focus down below inside this cube someplace. And the epicenter, now, is on the surface. Now, let's go back to the focus. Significance of the focus: That's where the earthquake occurred. That's where the fault movement occurred. That's where the energy was released. So the secret of the focus is that's where the energy is released during an earthquake. The epicenter, by definition now, is the point on the surface of the ground immediately above the focus. Note: If the focus is on the surface—like, remember, most earthquakes are and most faults are— then they would both be in the same place, but that's only fortuitous. The point is that the focus can be anywhere in depth—within limits, of course.

For example, let's say we made a chart with depth versus the number of earthquakes or the number of faults. And if you do that— remember, we said most of the faulting was in the first 40 miles of the Earth's crust—from the surface down to 40 miles of the Earth's crust. Those are called *shallow focus earthquakes* within that first 40 miles. Let's see, 75% of all the earthquakes are in that zone. Why? That's where the rocks are most brittle, that's what we're talking about here: breaking, you see. Then, from about 40 miles down to about 200 to 250 miles, note: The number of earthquakes drops off really fast—only about 20%. Why? The rocks are becoming more plastic, you see. They're starting to flow rather than break, and those are called *intermediate focus earthquakes*. And if you go below 250 miles down to about maybe 400 to 450 miles, there's only about 5% of earthquakes down there. They call them *deep focus earthquakes*. You don't have many because now the rocks are really, well, they're responding mostly, now, mostly by plastic flow is what they're doing. They're folding, perhaps, but they're not breaking—therefore if they don't break, you can't have a fault. Once you go below 450 miles, there are no earthquakes. Why? Because the rocks are totally plastic, and again if it's acting like a plastic, it's flowing; if it doesn't break, it's not going to give off one. So, anyway, there's the distribution of your earthquakes with depth.

Now, let's talk about different kinds of seismic waves. Let's go back to that focus business. At the focus of the earthquake, what's happening now—we'll picture this thing down in depth. It's sort of a general picture. So, here's the focus at some depth—who cares how far—but this is where the energy's going to be released now. The energy is released from the focus in the form of what we call *body waves.* Now, the body waves are both shear and compression. The shear waves are designated *s-waves,* the compression waves are designated *p-waves.* So, you have the S's and the P's. These are both moving away as body waves.

Now, here's the important thing: In terms of Earth movement—rock movement—the amount of energy that is being used to actually move the rocks as the body waves go through the body of the Earth, you see—that's why they're called body waves—is very, very, very little. My seismic guru tells me that the total amount of rock movement is on the order of, like, maybe a fraction of a millimeter: So, it's almost nothing. So, note: The point is: Of all the energy being released at the focus, very little is going to be wasted, if you will, moving rocks around. What's it going to be used for? Well, for anything else the thing wants to do—for example, moving itself. And, as a result of having all that energy, it turns out that these body waves go through the Earth very, very fast. Again, my seismic guru tells me that a body wave can travel from one side of the Earth completely through the center to the other side—remember now, that's 8,000 miles—and it can do it in something like 20 minutes. Well, just calculate that out, if I'm right, it comes out to something like 24,000 miles an hour. So, anyway, that's pretty fast.

Now, on the other hand, what's left with the rest of the energy, even that we don't use an awful lot of? So now, what happens to that energy? Note that the epicenter directly above now, directly above the focus—note what the significance of that is. Being directly above the focus that means that's the shortest distance that these body waves have to travel to get to the surface. So, it means that's where the most energy is going to be remaining in the body waves. And once the body waves get to the surface at the epicenter, it transfers the energy over to the surface, now, of the Earth and generates what we're going to call *surface waves.* So, the idea is, now, the maximum energy is at the epicenter. That's one of the whole things about the epicenter. You always hear they're always looking for it. The reason why they're looking for it is that's the point where the energy is the greatest.

Now as you go out in all directions from the epicenter, what's going to happen is the energy's going to drop off. Why? Well, it's doing things like moving the land around, and knocking buildings down, and scaring you, and all that kind of stuff. So it's using energy up. So

©2006 The Teaching Company Limited Partnership

the idea of the epicenter—that's where the energy is going to be greatest. But as you go out in all directions it's going to die off, and we'll talk about that next time when we talk about damage.

But anyway, let's go back to the epicenter now. What it does at the epicenter: The energy is transferred to the surface and creates surface waves—surface waves, now. Now the surface waves are totally different from the body waves. The main difference between them is the amplitude of the movement. Whereas the body waves move the rocks almost nothing, we're talking now about fairly large movements of the rocks: So large, as a matter of fact—we'll talk about this next time—but so large that, in some cases, you can actually see the surface wave moving across the surface of the Earth. Now you have to have a pretty good amplitude to see that. So, anyway, that's one of the big differences: You have very high amplitudes. Now, high amplitudes, you're burning up an awful lot of energy, so you're moving rocks around, and so those are going to die off pretty fast. As you go away from the epicenter, once again, the amplitudes are going to die off. So the maximum amplitude is going to be at the epicenter, and then it's going to die off as you go away—and that's what'll affect our discussion for next time.

What's the big difference between the surface waves—there are two kinds: Love and Rayleigh. Here's the difference between them. The *Love wave* is a shear wave, meaning the rocks are being moved perpendicular to the direction of propagation. So, let's picture now: The Love wave is moving away from you, across the surface of the Earth. It is a shear wave, so you're going to be moving the rocks back and forth, perpendicular to the direction of propagation, but only in the horizontal plane. See, not any of those others, only in the horizontal plane. So, as the Love wave goes across the surface of the Earth, the Earth is being moved back and forth, back and forth perpendicular to the direction in which the Love wave is going. Now, on the other hand, the Rayleigh wave is really the cool one. The *Rayleigh wave* what it is, it's a combination of the vertical component of shear—up and down—vertical component of shear plus that to and fro motion of compression. So, if you picture this one now: The motion of the Earth is going to be forward and up, backward and down, forward and up, backward and down. So it's going to be a crazy, rolling motion like that. So, both of those are going across the surface of the Earth simultaneously in all directions.

Now one of the things we're going to talk about in the next lecture is damage, but just sort of introduce it at this point. Question: Of those two kinds of surface waves, gut feeling, which one do you think would cause the most damage? I'll tell you the one I answered when I was a student and asked that question—of course, now, I always pick the wrong answer—but, anyway, that's another story. I picked the Rayleigh wave. Why? It just seemed to me that this shock wave going across the Earth, just undulating the ground like that, up and down like that, that must be wild. I mean it's got to tear buildings down and all kinds of stuff. Well, it just goes to show you, that isn't the right answer. The engineers tell us the big damager in earthquakes—of course, you're going to damage with the Rayleigh waves, too—but the bigger of the two, the biggest damage is caused by the Love waves. Now picture them: They're going back and forth, back and forth. That doesn't seem to be any big deal, but here's the thing. I think you can prove it to yourself with a very, very simple little experiment. Take a stack of dominos, and put it in your hand. This stack of dominos represents a tall building, a smokestack—I don't care what it is, it's some kind of a structure.

Now what you're going to do, if you're very careful, we're going to reproduce the Rayleigh motion, remember the to and fro—that kind of stuff? Very carefully if you've just got your hand and try to follow that sort of rotating, undulating motion. If you're very careful, you can get to the end, and the dominos are still there: In other words, they didn't come down. In other words, the destruction there was minimal. On the other hand, let's say you take the Love motion now. If that's the direction, let's say it's going away from you—remember now, it's moving it back and forth. Same stack of dominos now—the difference is, now, the Earth is moving to one side, and then back to the other side, and back to the other side again, and back and forth like that. Here's the picture now. Picture the Earth and the stack of dominos, now, going sideways, and then it's going to get to the end of the run, and then the Earth turns around and goes back the other way—but nobody told the stack of dominos. Remember inertia? "When in motion tends to keep you in motion." So here's the stack of dominos, which is your building or your smokestack. It's going in this direction. When the Earth turns around and goes back the other way, the domino stack keeps going in that direction and falls down. So, there's the reason why most of the damage is the result of the Love wave. It's that turnaround at the end that really kills you. It isn't the trip between the ends—it's that turnaround at the ends. So, combining those two, then, that's where the damage comes from, but when we get around to talking about damage due to earthquakes, just keep in mind that the Rayleigh wave, although got to do something, it's still a rolling motion, you see. But of the two, the Love wave does the greater amount of damage—but we'll talk about that next time when we get into the discussion of damage.

Lecture Thirty-One
Damage from Earthquakes

Scope:

Nothing is more terrifying than to experience an earthquake: feeling the Earth move, observing objects around you moving, and not knowing when or if it will all stop. Earthquakes, volcanic eruptions, and tropical storms represent nature at its furious best. All three are unpredictable as to where and when they will strike and what level of damage they will leave behind. All are potentially lethal, and we can do little to protect ourselves against their fury. The *intensity* and *magnitude* of an earthquake can be measured by means of the *Mercalli/Rossi scale* and the *Richter scale*. Various measures can be taken to protect structures from the damage caused by earthquakes, most of which is due to fires. Earthquakes can also generate tsunamis, which count among the most destructive phenomena in nature.

Outline

I.   The severity of an earthquake can be reported in terms of either *intensity* or *magnitude*.

    A. The intensity of an earthquake refers to the observed results of the quaking and the amount of resulting damage.

    B. An earthquake's magnitude involves determining the amount of Earth movement and the amount of energy released based on actual measurements of Earth movement.

    C. The first comprehensive study of earthquake intensity was performed by two seismologists, Rossi and Mercalli.

        1. The result of their studies were scales of damage, in which each step is a verbal description of what one would expect to experience or see. Because both scales were similar, their results were combined in what is referred to as the *Mercalli/Rossi scale* or the *modified Mercalli scale.*

        2. Using this scale, an earthquake of magnitude 1 will be detectable only by sensitive scientific instruments. Major but reparable damage will occur at a magnitude of 6. A magnitude of 8 would not leave many buildings standing. At a magnitude of 9, the shock wave is visible. In all of known history, there have been only four or five earthquakes of a magnitude of 9.

D. Another type of scale, the *Richter scale*, invented by Charles Richter, assigns a magnitude from 1.0 to 10.0, in which each next higher step in the scale represents 10 times the amount of Earth movement and 30 times the amount of energy released than the preceding step.

II. A great deal of research has gone into devising ways to build structures to resist earthquake damage. Realizing that there is no structure that is "earthquake proof," ways have been tested to minimize damage.

A. The type of building materials can affect the amount of damage.
   1. Buildings constructed of flexible materials, such as metal, have a better chance of survival.
   2. Wood is effective but is subject to destruction by fire.
   3. Steel and glass buildings, while flexible, are not practical because of the potential damage of the glass, which could rain down on the street.
   4. Masonry is too brittle.
   5. A compromise is the construction of masonry components around a metal framework that serves to distribute energy throughout the building, rather that allowing it to concentrate in one place.

B. Observations have shown that structures whose foundations are anchored in bedrock have a higher tendency to survive an earthquake than those whose foundations are in unconsolidated materials.
   1. During the 1989 Loma Prieta earthquake that struck San Francisco, one of the highly damaged areas of the city was the Marina District, where condominiums had been built on top of sediment deposited into the bay following the great earthquake and fire of 1906.
   2. Engineering studies have shown that such loose material, though compacted, has a tendency to momentarily turn to a gelatinous consistency as the shock wave passes.

C. In California, by law, buildings must be bolted to their foundations. Larger buildings in California have shock absorbers. Electrical and gas appliances, such as water heaters, must be strapped and bolted to a wall, because fire is the primary cause of damage during an earthquake (from leaking gas mains and so on).

D. Many lessons were learned from San Francisco's great earthquake of 1906. In that disaster, approximately 80% of the city was destroyed by the combination of fire and earthquake. Firefighters were unable to control fires throughout the city because their water mains were severed by the same earth movement that had severed the city's gas mains and fed the flames.

III. One of the most destructive earthquake-generated phenomena is the giant sea wave called a *tsunami*. Meaning "harbor wave" in Japanese, tsunamis are commonly referred to as "tidal waves," although they have nothing to do with the tides.

A. Most tsunamis are created by the release of earthquake energy from vertical fault movements within or along the margin of an ocean basin.

   1. Tsunamis cross the open sea with amplitudes rarely exceeding a foot but with speeds averaging 500 miles per hour.

   2. Upon reaching the shoreline, the increase in amplitude creates waves that can reach 100 feet high and drive onto land at speeds of more than 100 miles per hour, causing enormous destruction and death.

   3. The worst tsunami to hit the Japanese Islands occurred in 1896, when a wall of water estimated to be nearly 100 feet high crashed onto the eastern coastline of Honshu.

B. To warn inhabitants within and around the Pacific Ocean basin, the Seismic Sea Wave Warning System (SSWWS) was established in 1946. Earthquakes anywhere within or adjacent to the Pacific basin are monitored in Honolulu, Hawaii, with warnings broadcast throughout the Pacific.

C. Some tsunamis are generated by violent volcanic eruptions. The eruption of Krakatau in 1883, for example, generated a tsunami that washed over low-lying islands and swept more than 36,000 people to their deaths.

Recommended Reading:

Bryant, E., *Tsunami: The Underrated Hazard.*

Hough, S. E., *Earthquake Science: What We Know (and Don't Know) about Earthquakes.*

Questions to Consider:

1. Fire causes more earthquake damage than any other single factor. Why?

2. As a potential homebuilder in an earthquake-prone region, what features could you incorporate into the design of your home to minimize earthquake damage?

Lecture Thirty-One—Transcript
Damage from Earthquakes

Well, we're going to talk about damage due to earthquakes now. I think there are an awful lot of people who are probably very concerned about the damage part of it, especially if they live in an area where they might become part of it. First of all, there are two words that we use to describe earthquakes: one is intensity and the other is magnitude. Now, these are totally different. *Intensity* refers to the amount of damage that an earthquake causes. *Magnitude* involves the actual amount of Earth movement.

Now, we're going to talk about two different scales that measure these, and the first one we're going to talk about is the one that measures the damage. That's called the Mercalli/Rossi Scale, and a little bit later we'll talk about the one everybody hears about, that's the Richter Scale. The Richter Scale actually measures the amount of Earth movement and the amount of energy released. But let's talk about Mercalli/Rossi for a minute. Mercalli and Rossi were two seismologists. But here they are in the Mediterranean, I mean we're talking a big zone of subduction goes to the Mediterranean, so they have lots of earthquakes, and they had lots of opportunity to study these things. And they both did the same thing independently of each other. And basically what they did was this: There'd be an earthquake someplace, and they'd travel to wherever it was. And along the way, they would interview people who they ran into and ask them things like, "What did you see?" "What did you feel?" "What did you hear?" And then when they got close enough, they could see the damage for themselves, and they wrote all this stuff down. And so, in the end, what they ended up with was a scale where they had a relative scale now—"relative" means like one to 10, like Mohs's Scale of Hardness—and since they both did basically the same thing, sooner or later someone put them both together. So, now, we have the so-called Mercalli/Rossi Scale, and it—again—is a relative scale. I think it actually goes one to twelve, but let's say just one to ten, that's good enough. You get the idea. And so the thing is, if you look at the scale in a book, what you'll see is that each step in the scale is just sort of a verbal description of what you would see, or feel, or hear, had you been there—or what kind of damage you would observe—because that's they how they generated these things.

For example, number 1 on this scale always says something like, "Detected only by sensitive, scientific instruments." Well, the implication, of course, is that you could have an earthquake of number 1 on the Mercalli/Rossi Scale right under your foot, and you'd never know it. Why? Because you're not a sensitive, scientific instrument, I guess. Number 2 would say something like, "Detected by individuals sitting quietly at rest." Now, this is an interesting one because I have felt these in Morgantown, for example. Now, first of all, you usually have to be in the upper stories of a building so that you get the sway of the building. But in Morgantown, there have been many a time I'll be sitting up in my office late at night, and the building would just shudder like that. That's all it was. And it was just over that quickly.

And what it was in that case—well, one of the things we did a lot around Morgantown was mine coal. Most of the coal in the immediate area now is gone. But, nevertheless, when you mine coal, you dig a big hole underground, and take the coal out, and you've got these things called *rooms*. Well, sooner or later, the roof of these things collapses. Remember now, when it collapses there's a little tensional release, you see, a little bit of energy, a shudder goes through the rocks: not very much energy, but if you're sitting quietly you can feel it.

A 3 would say, "Felt by everyone." Now, the actual amount of movement is you could be walking down the street, and you can feel this one. A 4—by the time you get to a 4, things are starting to happen. For example, dishes on shelves would start to rattle around. Chandeliers would start to swing, if you've got one. Maybe little objects on a desk would start to move a little bit. There's no real damage yet, maybe a crack in a real plaster wall, but there aren't very many of those any more. A loose tile, for example, might fall out of the ceiling, but no great damage yet.

By the time you get to a 5—things are starting to happen now, at a 5. At a 5, those dishes that were rattling up on the shelf, they're on the floor. Things like cracks in the walls would start to appear now. Tiles would start coming down. Maybe a window or two would crack. Cracks would occur, let's say, in brick walls. Again, no great amount of damage, but still we're starting to see some stuff now. Someone always asks, "Can you be killed during a 5?" Well, of course, you can be killed anywhere if you're at the wrong place at the wrong time. If you're walking down the street, and a brick gets shook loose from the top of a building and comes down and hits you on the head, you're a goner. But normally at a 5 you're probably fairly safe.

But once you get to a 6, now, things are really going to start to happen. At a 6, you're going to start to see major damage to certain buildings. For example, if you have a building that's made of all ceramics—block, brick, or whatever, no supports in the walls—I would think a building like that would come down because you're going to crack a wall. Once that wall cracks, there's no support for it, and once that wall goes, the rest are going to follow. So, you're going to see damage like that. You're going to see major cracks in buildings. Even with steel superstructures, you're going to see major damage. But in that case, probably the damage could be repaired, so we're not into the non-repairable damage yet in major buildings, but you're going to see a lot of damage like that: cracks, and ceiling tiles come down, and windows going up.

By the time you get to a 7, now, at 7 you're starting to see some really bad stuff. For example, if you think back to the last earthquake that struck in the Los Angeles area, just north of the Los Angeles area, there were things like the overpasses came down, remember that? There was a parking garage that collapsed on itself. You're talking about some major stuff. The last earthquake that went through San Francisco, this would have been the Loma Prieta Earthquake, which was in 1989 or thereabouts. When it went through the San Francisco area, remember, it collapsed those big posts on the Nimitz Freeway, and the thing came down and squashed cars. You're talking big-time damage. There are not very many buildings that will withstand, without some major damage, at a 7.

An 8—by the time you get up to an 8 you're talking, now, major earthquake. I think that people who really study earthquakes consider 8 to be the major. A 7 is bad, but 8 is a major earthquake. There really aren't very many buildings that you can build that will withstand an 8. I'm just thinking, for example, in the Morgantown area—I don't think they build anything in that area that will withstand an 8. You're talking about super damage now. We'll talk a little bit about the Great San Francisco Earthquake and Fire: That was supposedly on the Richter Scale, which we'll talk about in a second, somewhere just about over 8 and, you know, 80% to 90% of the city was destroyed. So, anyway, we're talking big-time.

A 9—at a 9, now, the energy is so great that you can actually see the shock wave moving across Earth's surface, going up and down and back and forth. I don't care what you build, and I don't care how you build it, you hit it with a 9 and it's coming down. Fortunately for all concerned as you go up these scales, the number of earthquakes in each category decreases exponentially. For example, the last 9 was the one that hit over there in the Indonesian zone of subduction: The one that wiped out or damaged very badly Sri Lanka—that was a 9. And it seems to me I read at the time someone had tabulated that in all of known time, in known history, there have only ever been about five or six 9's—fortunately, because that would be about as much destruction as you could possibly imagine. The 10, of course, would be an unattainable limit. The 10's are only reached in movies kind of thing. So, anyway, that would be basically the Mercalli/Rossi Scale. It's simply a damage thing.

Now, the other one, the one you hear about all the time, however, is the Richter Scale. Now, that was Charles Richter, see this would have been the mid-30s sometime. He was a professor of seismology, I believe, at the California Institute of Technology. And he came up with this scale based upon actual Earth movements now, and also experiments he actually conducted in the lab where he subjected rocks to compression and tension to get a feel for how much energy it took to break them up. Based upon those kinds of observations, he came up with the so-called "Richter Scale." The original Richter Scale, again, was a 1 to 10 kind of thing, and the numbers between the two scales, I think, are pretty close. A 3 in the Richter is a 3 in the Mercalli, and back and forth like that. But here's the big difference: What the Richter Scale measures is not damage. What the Richter Scale measured is two things: actual Earth movement and energy released.

Now, here's all you have to remember about the Richter Scale. Every time you step up one on the Richter Scale you multiply the actual amount of Earth movement by 10. So, for example, let's say we were talking a minute ago about Rossi's Scale. Well, a 1, the motion is so small that you wouldn't feel it all. But note: When you went to a 2, you multiplied that motion by 10, and now the motion is such that if you were sitting quietly you might feel it. But if you multiply that by 10, now everybody feels it. So just think about that. You're going up the scale, 10 x 10 x 10 x 10. By the time you get to a 9, the amount of actual movement is great enough that you can see it: You can see the Earth going up and down and back and forth. So, in other words, that's sort of a way to look at it. So it's a big difference, for example, between a 7 and an 8—10 times the Earth movement.

But on the other hand, it's also energy, and I think this is probably what you have to really consider. It's the amount of energy we have to deal with. Well, here's all you have to remember there: Every time you step up the Richter Scale you're multiplying the amount of energy by 30—30 times. So think about that now: multiplying 30 x 30 x 30 x 30. By the time you get to a 9, the number is humongous. The amount of energy represented in an earthquake of a 9 on the Richter Scale is almost beyond comprehension. So, anyway, that's the thing to remember. The next time you see these numbers or hear these numbers, just think about that. Every step up is 10 x the amount of Earth movement, and every step up is 30 x the amount of energy released.

So, anyway, a question: Can you build anything to withstand that? Let me just start off by saying there's no such thing as an "earthquake-proof" anything. I don't care what you build, and I don't care how you build it, you hit it with a 9, and it's coming down. Nothing we can build can possibly withstand that.

Well then, how about earthquake resistance? Well, yes, there's been an awful lot of work done on this for an awful long time. Engineers have worked on this for years, and well tens, and probably 100 years. For example, if you want something to withstand an earthquake shock wave, what you want to pick is something that's very flexible. You don't want to pick something that's very brittle, you see. You don't want it to break. So, for example, if we had to pick something very common that would be very flexible, wood would be really good. The problem with wood is it burns. And one of the things we're going to talk about before we're done here is the fact of the matter is that fire is the most damaging aspect of an earthquake. That's what causes most of the damage. A lot of people think it's the movement of the rocks. No, the movement of the rocks, what the movement of the rocks does—that movement sets off a sort of a domino kind of effect that ends up in fires and fires cause the big damage. So you don't want to use wood. A thing I think probably is pretty good are these all-metal buildings, for example, in Pittsburgh we have the Alcoa Building or the U.S. Steel Building. Those things would just sort of wave back and forth: very, very flexible. The problem I see with some of those buildings, however, is that what they do with them for architectural beauty, they sheath them on the outside with glass or, I guess, plastic. And I can just picture one of these things waving back and forth, and that glass or that plastic sheath popping off the outside, raining down onto the sidewalks and the streets below like so many guillotines. Do I have to describe the scenario at street level? That would be very, very, very bad.

Something you want to absolutely avoid: masonry buildings, all masonry buildings. For example, I'm thinking: In Morgantown, there are buildings that are just cinderblock covered with brick to make them look a little bit better. No supports in the walls, none whatsoever. Supports perhaps in the floor, steel, but nothing in the walls. You hit that with a 6, 6.5, you're going to crack one wall, and then the rest is going to come down.

Now, better than that is, of course, the steel superstructure. Most of the big buildings, of course, have this steel super structure, and then you put the masonry around that. Now, the secret of that is that the steel is able to sort of distribute the energy throughout the building and doesn't allow it to concentrate in any one place. That way it preserves these cracks we're talking about that would be very, very disastrous. On the other hand, if you did have a crack, then you still have steel around that portion of the building to sort of hold things together. So most of the buildings you would build, large ones anyway, are going to be built that way.

Now, here's another thing. We have found an awful lot out about what to do and what not to do. They have found out a long, long time ago, for example, that buildings that have foundations anchored in bedrock, those will survive much better than those that are not. For example, I'm thinking, now, of that last earthquake that went through San Francisco as a result of the Loma Prieta. If you think about the damage that was reported in San Francisco, the only real damage in the city, now, in the city, was to an area called the Marina. Now, what the Marina was—still is—it's a place where they have all these condos. It's now down next to the Bay. But here's what it is: It's simply loose-packed debris that was simply put into the Bay as a result of the 1906 earthquake. What they did, they cleaned the place up and dumped all the debris into the Bay, packed it down and made more land, and put condos on it. Now, here's what the engineers have found long, long since. If you have loose, unconsolidated material like that, and especially if it's water saturated like that would be—you see, the Bay's just right there, and especially if it's water saturated—you put a shock wave through it, under those conditions this material that would bear a lot of weight from above, they compacted it down, you see.

All of a sudden, this stuff just turns into something they describe like Jell-O™. There's no supporting strength to it, you see, just momentarily, but that's all you have to have. If the sub-base at which you're buildings are set just turns to something that has no supporting capacity, the buildings are just going to settle right down into it. Now, it only takes a few seconds, but that's all you need. So here we have the picture of the Marina. You've all seen the pictures of it, I'm sure: You see, these buildings, they're hanging out over the street; they're tipping to one side or the other. That's what happened down there. You don't build buildings on things like that if you want them to withstand an earthquake shock wave. Loose materials like that are very, very, very bad.

Here's another thing they saw a long time ago, too. There was always a complaint that buildings were "falling off their foundations." Well, I'm not sure that's exactly what happened. Picture, if you will, a building on a foundation. And let's say we have a Love wave coming through now. The Love wave's come, let's say, away from you. And, of course, the Earth's surface is moving back and forth, right to left, and here's the foundation of the building with the building now. Let's say it moves over here to the left, and then it goes back to the right: Well, the foundation goes back to the right, but remember inertia? The building didn't know about that return business, and so the building just keeps right on going. So inertia takes over, and what happens is the building didn't "fall off" the foundation. The foundation was pulled out from under the building. That's what really happened.

Well, the interesting thing is if you go to California, they're probably the best state, probably in the world, in terms of designing things to withstand earthquakes. Why? 90% of all the earthquake energy released in the southern 48 is released in California: Most of it is directly associated with that San Andreas Fault zone we talked about, and it's a live fault. So, anyway, what they've done, they've done to, say, decrease the amount of damage. For example, if you go to

California, the law says that if you build a building—I don't care what size it is, even a one-family building for a home—you've got to bolt it to the foundation. I don't know if you realize this or not, and I don't know where you live, but chances are very good your house, like my house, just sits on the foundation. It's just the weight of the house alone that keeps it there. But you see, you can't count on that in someplace like California. You can't count on that in any place where you're going to have the potential of an earthquake like that. So in California, the law is you have to actually bolt the building to the foundation regardless of what size it is, even a one-family home or a skyscraper—they all have to be fixed to the foundation.

And then the larger buildings, in the larger buildings what they actually do, they have between the building itself and the foundation, shock absorbers. Now, I've read where they used huge rubber grommets and even springs, and the idea is: The shock wave traveling through the Earth to get to the building has got to go through from the foundation to the building. But what happens is, of course, the shock absorbers and the springs do exactly the same thing to the building that the shock absorbers and springs do with your car. You're driving down a really, really rough road, and your wheels are going all over the place, but your car, the one you're riding in, is just moving along very nicely. Why? The energy of all those impacts with the road is being absorbed by the shock absorbers and by the springs. So they do that out there with the large, large buildings.

Well, anyway, here's another thing they require in California, and I think this sort of leads us into our next topic. Hot water heaters—I don't know what yours looks like, but most hot water heaters are these great big tall tanks obviously pretty top heavy. You cannot have, in the state of California, a hot water heater just sitting on the floor wherever that is, basement or whatever. The possibility of it being knocked over is too high. If it's knocked over, then whatever feeds the energy to it—whether it's gas or electricity—there's always the potential for fire, and that's what you've got to prevent. You've got to keep that to an absolute minimum. And to give you a good example—and I think if we just sort of very briefly recall the great San Francisco earthquake and fire of 1906—this is a beautiful example of the fact that fire is the number one damager in an earthquake. So here's the picture of California and San Francisco in 1906. San Francisco was the biggest-growing city out on the West

Coast. It was the port of entry for anybody who was coming into that part of the world. It was fast-growing. They were already building skyscrapers—seven and eight stories high with steel frameworks, the whole bit. So they were moving right along. But still, most of the city, interestingly enough, was built of wood. As a matter of fact, they used to call themselves "The Largest Wooden City in the World." But anyway, most of the buildings are wood. Now, what they would do on the fronts of the buildings, facing the street, is they would put a façade maybe—of stone or brick to make it look somewhat more substantial. But in the back, it was still made of wood.

Another thing they did in San Francisco that they were very, very proud of: Here we were in the early part of the 1900s, electric lights were coming on to the scene, and even at that time, apparently some of the downtown streets were lit by these newfangled electric lights. And I'm sure some of the wealthy people had them in their homes, too. But the fact of the matter is that most of the city was lit by gas lamps and kerosene lamps.

Another thing they were very proud of was their firefighting system. You know, you see the old movies, when there's a fire, and out from the fire station come these horse-drawn carriages, and one has all the ladders on them, one has a steam engine on it, and one has a big tank of water because they had to haul the water to the fire. Well, what they did in San Francisco very early in the game is they built this system of water piping and hydrants throughout the city, and they had pumps down at the Bay that was pumping water into these all the time. So they had this water pumped throughout the city, and as a matter of fact, I think they actually even had up on the high tops, like Nob Hill, actually reservoirs like the old city water supply we talked about. So, anyway, they were very proud of this thing.

So then what happened? Let's see, this would have been early in the morning, something like 5:00 in the morning on the 18th of April in aught six. The San Andreas Fault gave a lurch. Now, the maximum movement of the San Andreas Fault during that particular earthquake was about, I believe, 15 feet. The epicenter of it was north of the city, up around Point Reyes. And so that's where the big 15 feet were. But the shock wave sort of goes through the city, of course. So then you have to sort of picture what's going to happen now: Shock wave goes through the city, we're talking here, undoubtedly—the

Richter Scale wasn't in existence yet, but we can sort of backtrack and sort of calculate probably what it was. I would say probably in 8, 8.1, 8.2—certainly in the low 8's. So the shock wave goes through the city: The first thing that happens is lanterns are toppled over in homes, you see—kerosene lamps fall onto the floor, and burst, and set the place on fire. Then what happens, of course, here you have the buildings, now, are burning. Then, if you ever go to San Francisco, it's not exactly really steep, but they have fairly steep hillsides, and all of a sudden, you start having these slumps: no big landslides necessarily, but slumps. And the result was the slumps severed the gas mains that were feeding the gas of these buildings, you see. All of a sudden these fires have started that were now being fed by gas that was leaking from these gas mains.

And then what happened? Well, of course, the fire department takes off to go out to fight the fires—right off the bat they're in trouble because a lot of those façades from the fronts of those buildings have fallen down in the street. So they couldn't even get through to a lot of the streets. And then when they finally got to some of the places where they could get and hooked up these fire hydrants, they found out too late that that same movement that severed the gas mains also severed their water mains. All the water had drained out of their newfangled firefighting system. So here they were fighting fires with nothing—they had no water. They were trying to pump water from the Bay, for example, but they just couldn't pump enough of it fast enough. So the city is on fire, and it raged like that for days, and days, and days. They finally got it stopped by dynamiting down whole blocks of the city, making like fire breaks: You know what a fire break is in a forest? You go through a forest, and you'll see that it looks like a big roadway, but there's no road in there—that's basically a *fire break*. The idea is that when forest fires move through a forest, they don't move along the ground really—most of them they crown from treetop to treetop. So if you can chop down a bunch of trees and keep it from jumping across to the other side, you have a chance to get it stopped. Well, basically, that's how they finally got the fire stopped in San Francisco. But by that time 90% of the city was destroyed, note: by fire. It wasn't the actual movement of the fault that really did it because the fault is on the other side of the peninsula. People say it goes under San Francisco. No, the San Andreas Fault does not go under San Francisco. So, I think there's the perfect example of fire being the number one damager in the case of earthquakes.

So, anyway, one of the last things I want to talk about in terms of damage—and we have to do this because this is a big, big source of damage—are tsunamis. Now *tsunami*, of course, is a sea wave. As a matter of fact, the name *tsunami* in Japanese means harbor wave: harbor, because that's where most of the damage they experienced was in harbors. But, anyway, what a tsunami is, it's a sea wave. It can be generated two ways: earthquakes, of course, are one and also volcanic eruptions. But these volcanic eruptions or earthquakes have to occur within the basin of—or close to the basin of—the ocean. Picture, for example, the one that ended up destroying much of Sri Lanka. That happened in the Indonesian zone of subduction, right there on the edge of the Indian Ocean. So the idea is that whenever this movement occurs along that zone of subduction—remember, we talked about that great big thrust fault, you see, or reverse fault—a lot of that energy is delivered right to the ocean wave, to the water. Now think about making waves. Normally, you make waves by blowing air across the water, and you transfer energy out of the air into the water. That's where the waves get their energy. Now we're talking big-time energy: We're talking an absolutely enormous amount of energy stored in these wave forms. The wave takes off. Now, here's the interesting thing about these tsunamis. They have so much energy, they cross the ocean at speed of about maybe 500 to 600 miles per hour. That's almost hard to imagine.

Now the amplitude is very, very small. You could be out in the middle of the ocean when one of these things goes by, and in a rowboat, you'd probably never know it. But the idea is now coming onto shore. When it comes onto shore, picture now just an average coast—we've all walked down to the beach—you see the waves coming on shore. As soon as the wave form touches the bottom out there somewhere, the first thing that happens is the amplitude starts to build, and you start to make these higher and higher. And then you go into the breakers. And finally that crashes up on the shore. You can just sit and watch that. The process is exactly the same. The only differences are two things: It starts building further out to sea, and—number two—you've got enormous amounts of energy. So what's happening—this building of the water, the making of these breakers—they're enormous. You're talking about walls of water coming at you at velocities of over 100 miles per hour at elevations in the tens of feet, 30–40–50 feet. The biggest one I could find record of—it came on Honshu Island, this would have been back in, I think it was something like 1896. They describe a wall of water coming on shore 100 feet high. Now I can't even imagine, 100 feet high coming at you at over 100 miles per hour. You're really in trouble now, you see. Of course, it's incompressible, you see, so that's like being hit with a wall of concrete doing 100 miles per hour. Well, the destruction was enormous. I don't know how many people were killed on Honshu.

But, anyway, this is an enormous thing. So, that flooding onto the shoreline—that's what causes the damage. Now, as a result of that—most of these happen, of course, around the Pacific Ocean because, remember, that's where most of the zones of subduction are. So way back in about 1946, I think it was, they set up a warning system for all of the islands and the peripheral people of the Pacific Ocean basin, and it was called the *Seismic Sea Wave Warning System*. And what it was—well, the way it works is there's an earthquake, let's say it happens in one of the zones of subduction—well, they can pick out the time when that happens right off the bat. And then, of course, there are buoys that they have out in the ocean that detect this thing as it goes by. Then once they see how fast it's going and the direction it's going, then they can send warnings to everybody in its path. And if you ever go to the Island of Hawaii, for example, the warning or sirens that go off: If you're ever in Hawaii, and the sirens go off, the object of the game is to get to high ground as fast as you can. Because, see, that's the problem. These people that were in Sri Lanka, they had no warning. Why? There was no warning system in the Indian Ocean. They didn't know it was coming. Some people recognized something was going wrong because when those breakers started building offshore, the water ran off from the beach area. That doesn't usually happen, you see. That was the first indication to anybody that something really nasty was going to happen. Well, you see, they have a warning system in the Pacific Ocean, and the warning system is such that any low-lying area can be warned with these sirens. So, again, if you're ever in Hawaii and the sirens go off, get out of the way because there's a tsunami coming, you see. Well, they're actually talking now about putting one around the Indian Ocean. Now, of course, hindsight is a wonderful thing. It always is. It's 20/20 vision, you see.

But, anyway, the other one I just want to comment on is volcanic eruptions. Any large-scale volcanic eruption anywhere near the ocean will generate one of these things, too. For example, I remember reading about Krakatoa. Krakatoa was a volcanic island in the Indonesian chain, and it erupted back in 1883, I believe it was. This had to be, now, a Plinian-type eruption—remember, the biggest one we could imagine. It generated a sea wave that took off, and the sea wave just swamped all the low-lying islands in the area. And it's estimated that 36,000 people died because of that one sea wave. The sea wave, then, was detected all the way as far as San Francisco Bay. This is just one volcanic eruption. So these things are very, very, very potent. The tsunami is, without a doubt, one of the single most damaging features that's created by earthquakes. So, anyway, there's a pretty good picture for you about what kind of damage you'd expect if you live in an earthquake-prone area.

Lecture Thirty-Two
Seismology

Scope:

Earthquakes have been detected for centuries with the use of seismometers, but the ability to study the full impact of earthquakes awaited the invention of a seismograph that would not only detect but actually measure Earth movement. Early seismographs could not record the time-related component of the earthquake. This problem was solved in the late 1800s by John Milne, who replaced the flat recording surface with a rotating cylinder. To record horizontal motion, the instrument was designed with a horizontally suspended pendulum. To record vertical movement, a pendulum was suspended vertically. Milne's design provided the basis of modern seismographs, which are synchronized across the globe with caesium clocks. The seismograms they produce enable the seismologist to determine the epicenter, focus, and magnitude of the earthquake, although they cannot predict an earthquake with any useful level of precision.

Outline

I. *Seismology* is the study of earthquakes, and the instruments seismologists have used to study Earth movements are the *seismometer* and the *seismograph*.

   A. An instrument whose name ends in -*graph* gives a permanent record of whatever was measured in the form of a -*gram*, while an instrument whose name ends in -*meter* measures but does not provide a recording of any kind.

      1. A seismograph provides a seismogram, while a speedometer provides no record.

      2. Seismometers existed long before the invention of the seismograph. The first seismometer was invented by the Chinese sometime in the 2nd century. Seismometers were the tools of the trade for nearly 1,500 years.

   B. Sometime in the mid-1700s, the first seismograph was invented. The basic design was improved upon in 1858 by an Italian physicist named Cavalleri, who used two pendulum-based instruments to record the maximum amplitude of both horizontal and vertical Earth motions.

1. Cavalleri's instrument consisted basically of a ring stand from which the pendulums were suspended, one on a string and the other on a spring. A pen extending from the pendulum drew a line on a piece of paper. The passage of the Love and Rayleigh waves would move the ring stand, while the pendulums, because of their inertia, would remain motionless.

2. The instrument with the pendulum suspended on a string recorded the passage of a Love wave by drawing a line on a piece of paper placed on the base of the ring stand.

3. The instrument with the pendulum suspended on a spring recorded the passage of a Rayleigh wave by drawing a line on a piece of paper attached to the upright of the ring stand.

4. Combined, these two devices measured the amplitude and direction of the shock waves. The major shortcoming of these seismographs was the fact that they could not record any time-related component of an earthquake.

C. The problem of recording time-related events was solved in the late 1800s by an English engineer named John Milne, who replaced the flat recording surface with a rotating cylinder to which the recording paper was attached.

1. To record the horizontal motions of Love waves, Milne designed an instrument with a pendulum suspended horizontally.

2. The vertical movement of Rayleigh waves was recorded with a vertical-pendulum instrument comparable to Cavalleri's.

3. As the cylinder was *rotated* and *translated* (moved sideways) along its axis by a clock mechanism, the recording pen scribed a timed, spiraling line on a piece of paper wrapped around the cylinder.

4. When removed from the cylinder and laid flat, the resultant seismogram recorded seismic history over a period of time.

D. The modern seismic station consists of two horizontal-pendulum instruments oriented at right angles to each other and one vertical-pendulum instrument. The two horizontal instruments allow the recording of Love waves approaching from any direction. The vertical motion of the Rayleigh waves is recorded by the vertical-pendulum instrument.

1. All seismograms are accurately timed by the recording of a signal sent out from synchronized caesium clocks, one of which is located at the Bureau of Standards at Fort Collins, Colorado.

2. The fact that all seismographs worldwide are tuned to the same clock allows seismograms from around the world to be compared.

II. The two bits of information a seismologist wants to glean from every seismogram are the location of the epicenter and focus and the magnitude of the earthquake at the epicenter.

A. The distance from a seismic station to the epicenter is determined by using the different arrival times of the p- and s- body waves and the data from a time-travel plot available at the recording station. (The body waves arrive faster than the surface waves, and the p-wave [compression wave] is faster than the s-wave [shear wave].)

1. The geographic location of the epicenter is determined by using the distance data from a minimum of three seismic stations plotted as a circle centered at the respective stations.

2. By using the distance data as the radius of a hemisphere centered on the respective stations, the point where the three hemispheres intersect is the location of the earthquake focus.

B. The magnitude of the earthquake at the epicenter can be determined from the data recorded at a *single* seismic station.

1. The amplitude of the surface waves will be at a maximum at the epicenter and decrease away from the epicenter in a predictable fashion. Determining the amplitude of the surface waves at a particular seismic station and knowing how far away the earthquake occurred enables scientists to calculate the amplitude of the surface waves at the epicenter.

2. The amplitude of the surface waves at the epicenter can then be used to calculate the Richter scale reading

(giving the magnitude). The actual determination employs the use of a *nomograph*.

III. Like so many geologic events, including volcanic eruptions and slope failures, earthquakes cannot be predicted with the level of precision that would be of use to those potentially involved.

Recommended Reading:

Bryant, E., *Tsunami: The Underrated Hazard*.

Hough, S. E., *Earthquake Science: What We Know (and Don't Know) about Earthquakes*.

Questions to Consider:

1. Why are two mutually perpendicular/horizontal-pendulum instruments required to record all incoming seismic waves?

2. What allows the data from a single seismic station and a simple nomograph to be used to estimate the Richter scale reading at a distant earthquake's epicenter?

Lecture Thirty-Two—Transcript
Seismology

Seismology is the study of earthquakes. Actually it probably has some more practical applications today just in passing. For example, the same principles we're going to talk about are used by folks at the oil industry to determine the presence of sub-surface structures. What they do is they generate their own shock waves either by setting up some of kind of a charge—or they have things called *thumpers* that generate a shock wave that goes down to these sub-surface structures and bounces back. But the equipment looks very, very, very much the same as the equipment we're going to describe here.

Let me describe, first of all, the difference between two instruments. There's a thing called a *seismometer*, and then there's a thing called a *seismograph*. Now the deal is any time you see an instrument and it has the word *meter*—like seismo*meter*, or speedo*meter*, or volt*meter*—what that is, it's an instrument that will measure something for you and tell you what it is, but there's no record left after it's all said and done. For example, like a voltmeter you put the prongs into your outlet, and it says 110, 220, and you pull them out, and it goes back to zero again. So that's a *meter*. Now a *graph* is an instrument that measures something for you, but it also gives you some kind of a recording; like a tele*graph* gives you a tele*gram*. The *gram* is the recording of a graph. Anyway, seismographs give you seismograms.

Let's talk about the seismometer first. These have been around for a long, long time. The Chinese have been studying earthquakes for many, many moons. And so I think the first seismometer dates back to something like the 2nd century. I remember when I was in China for a meeting a number of years ago, and they took us to Xian, which is their big research center for seismology, and they showed us one of these things. They said theirs was the oldest of the bunch in China. And what it was, it was a sphere—I guess it may have been 2 ½ or 3 feet in diameter—and around the equator of the sphere, there were arranged these brass dragons. And the dragons had their mouths open, you know, with the great big teeth in the front, and they had a brass ball just balanced right between those two front teeth. And then down below each dragon, on the base of the instrument, there were these frogs looking up with their mouths opened.

Now the way this thing worked—let's imagine, for example, you're standing in front of this seismometer, and a shock wave comes by moving away from you. This would be a Love wave now. Moving the ball and the whole thing back and forth, right to left—like that—right to left. Well, the idea is that the dragons, now, which would be lined up with the direction in which the shock wave was moving, now, they would be going side to side, like that. And the ball sitting between their two front teeth would be stabilized by their two teeth, and it would not fall out. Think about, now, the dragons who were on the other side, 90° to that. They're going back and forth like that, and they're going in and out like that. And inertia takes over again, and as the dragon goes forward the ball goes with it. But then the dragon backs up, and the ball keeps going. And so the ball would fall out of the dragon's mouth, and then down into the mouth of the frogs. I guess the frogs were simply there, so they didn't have to run around the place looking for the balls after it was all over.

Anyway, that's the way it worked. Now, what did it tell them? Well it told them it had been an earthquake, okay. And as a matter fact, note, it also told them in general which direction the shock wave came from. It either was going away from you or toward you, and that was a lot of information just for a ball like that. Anyway, that's what the seismometer looked like. And that's the way it was for a long, long time. It was going to take—well I think it must have been late in the 1700s or into the 1800s when someone was trying figure out, how do we make something better than that? How do we make something that's really going to measure the movement of the Earth and at the same time give us some kind of a record?

I asked a physicist friend of mine that: "Why did it take so long?" And he told me an interesting thing about instruments used to measure the motion of some other body. He said that what you have to do is some part of this body we're talking about has to be going in a known direction at a known velocity (I guess sort of a reference you can use); or B, there has to be some part of this body (we're talking about this instrument), which remains absolutely motionless when everything else is moving. Now, the first thing that popped in mind was, "I don't think so." I mean I've got a speedometer in my car, and I can drive down the road, and it's telling me I'm doing 50 or 60 miles an hour, and there's no part of that speedometer that's going in a known direction and a known speed. And there sure isn't any part of it standing still when I'm driving down the road at 50 miles an hour. And then he said, "Yes there is, there has to be—otherwise it wouldn't work." He pointed out to me that the part of the speedometer that's in the dashboard—that's only part of the speedometer. There's another part—it's a cable, a flexible cable that goes to your transmission, measures how many times that turns over. And then the transmission is connected through a drive rod to a differential, and that's connected through axles to wheels. And on these wheels, you have these tires. Now all of that, admittedly now, is going down the road with me, so we haven't found the part that's standing still yet. But then he said—and it just then dawned on me—"Here you have a tire with a tread, which—because of the tread and the roughness—actually sticks to the road by friction." All of a sudden, now, the pavement becomes part of the speedometer because it's fixed to that tire; if it wasn't for that pavement standing still, your speedometer would tell you nothing.

For example, depending upon where you live in the country, you probably have had this experience: snow and ice in the wintertime. You're coming up a hill hoping to get to the top, and all of a sudden your tires or wheels hit an ice spot. All of a sudden you lose traction, you see, and the wheels start spinning. What do you do at that moment? You jam it to the floor, hoping to burn through the ice to get back to the pavement. Now, if you could look at your speedometer at that moment, it would be pegged, 200 miles an hour. Are you doing 200 miles an hour forward? No, you're doing about 2 miles an hour backward, and you're ready to back into a parked car. So note: Once you remove that pavement, it's all over. Your speedometer tells you nothing.

Well, it probably doesn't come as a surprise, then, that the one who figured out how to do this was a physicist. And here's what he did, this is very, very, simple—the best inventions always are. So picture, if you will, two ring stands. Okay, two ring stands. What we're going to do is we're going to hang from one ring stand a pendulum on a string, that's with a t —and on the other one, we're going to hang from the ring stand another pendulum on a spring with a p. Now the thing about a pendulum: It's a large mass of material. Because of high mass it's got lots of inertia, which, note—when at rest tends to keep things at rest. So let's take the first one, hanging on the string, now. Out from the bottom, now, of the pendulum comes some kind of a pen, and on the bottom, now, of the ring stand there's a piece of a paper, and the pen just barely touches the piece of paper. So it's sitting there. Now a shock wave comes through: Let's, again, think of a Love wave that's moving away from you. Now it's moving the Earth back and forth, right to left like that, and what it does as it moves back and forth, the ring stand moves with that piece of paper moving back and forth, but the pendulum now remains stationary. So what happens is a line is drawn on the piece of paper.

The significance of the line: First of all, the length of the line, that's how much Earth movement we're dealing with. So, that line measures the amplitude, now, of the Love wave. The other thing it tells—note: The direction from which the shock wave came is perpendicular to that, so we know, now, that the shock wave came one of two directions. It either was going away from you, or coming toward you. Now, you don't know which one of those it is because there are two ends to every line, but note: You've eliminated all the other possibilities all the way around. That's an awful lot of information from a single little instrument like that.

Now, the other one, how about the Rayleigh wave? Remember that's the up and down motion. So here's the only difference; over here now you have this pendulum suspended on a spring. Out from the back end of the pendulum comes another pen point. There's a piece of a paper with some kind of a mount mounted on the upright now of the ring stand, and now, here again, the picture. As the Rayleigh wave goes by, moving the Earth up and down, the paper with the whole ring stand, you see, is moving up and down. The pendulum, now, remains stationary because of the high inertia. So now we draw a line on the paper, and note what that line is. That basically is the amplitude of the Rayleigh wave. So note, from these two simple instruments not only do you have the amplitude of the Love wave, you've got the amplitude of the Rayleigh wave, plus you've got the direction from which the shock wave came—one of two, one of two. I'd say that's an awful lot of information from some simple instrument like that.

Problem—note: There's nothing recorded that has anything to do with time. For example, when did the shock wave arrive? Unless you're standing there, of course, when it did. When did it arrive? There's no record of that. How long did the shock wave last? There's no record of that. How did the amplitude change with time? You can't tell that either. So nothing that occurred with time can be recorded—but, nevertheless, that's a big, big step over the balls falling out of the mouths of dragons, you see.

Okay, so where was it then? Well that's the way it stayed for—well, actually into the later part of the 1800s, I guess. Onto the scene came an Englishman by the name of John Milne. John Milne was an English engineer, and the story goes that he went to Japan once Japan opened its doors to the Western world. And of course he was there in Japan, which receives more earthquakes than anybody—they're sitting right on the biggest zone of subduction there is right off shore, you see. And so he was experiencing all these earthquakes, and he wanted to study these earthquakes. He knew about these two very simple instruments that had already been made. He knew about the shortcomings of them. And so he wanted to come up with an instrument that would actually record time. So here's all he did. This is actually pretty ingenious, too.

He made an instrument where he suspended the pendulum—not vertically, but on a bar. The pendulum was out at the end of a bar, suspended horizontally. The bar now could pivot back at the other end, so the pendulum could swing in a horizontal plane. Now, of course, the pendulum doesn't move—remember the pendulum stands still. Then under the pendulum, there was a pen that came out from the pendulum. And under the pendulum, fixed to the bottom of the instrument, he put a cylinder that rotated, driven by a clock. So picture now, let's say, this thing is rotating once a day. So, you put a piece of a paper on this drum, and you put the pen from the pendulum down on the drum, and you start it going. In one day it would make one revolution. Now, if nothing happened during that day, you'd take the piece of paper off, and there's a straight line: It tells you nothing happened.

But what if during that particular day as it's recording, all of a sudden, a shock wave comes through? And this shock wave, now, is moving parallel to the arm of that pendulum. Note: The base of the instrument goes back and forth—that's the Love wave, you see, and the cylinder moves back and forth. The pendulum and the pen stay stationary, and it draws a line, but now it's a squiggly line that's being drawn on that piece of paper around that cylinder. So, now you take the piece of paper off, and here comes the line straight across, and all of a sudden, here a squiggly line starts—and then it ends, and then it continues on to the end. That records the beginning and the end of the earthquake, so you can tell when it started and when it stopped. He could actually measure the change in the amplitude of the wave as it went through, and the earthquake continued. So now he had an instrument that recorded time. That was important.

Now, here's the deal. Let's say this instrument recorded one day, 24 hours. But you don't want to change paper every day. You want it to record for a week, seven days, let's say. All right, so here's all you do, and this was the ingenious part about it—not only did he rotate this drum, but while it was rotating it was moving sideways. We call that *translation*. So if you picture, now, a rotating and translating drum, if you just do it with your finger, make your finger go in sort of a spiral, and that's what the pen would have been drawing on the cylinder; a spiraling line from one end to the other. Now you take the piece of paper off, there are seven lines across the paper, one for each day, and now you have seven days. If, within that seven-day period, an earthquake would appear, there it is—you can time it. So, the idea is that you can now have long recordings of instruments.

Now the interesting thing is the modern instrument is not much different from that. The only thing we've taken advantage of now, of course: computers and all that sort of thing. But that basic instrument is still used today. Now here's the problem with the instrument we just described: Remember now, the shockwave is coming parallel to the arm of the pendulum. The instrument and the cylinder are moving back and forth, and the pendulum is remaining stationary. What would happen now if, let's say, the instrument was sitting in front of you sort of east-west or right-to-left? Now the shock wave comes through, away from you again, and now the whole instrument starts to move back and forth along with the pendulum. The pendulum is no longer stationary, see, so would that instrument record anything? No, it won't. So what do you do? Well, what you do is you take two instruments like that, and you put them at right angles to each other, so between these two instruments, you can record shock waves coming in from any angle you want. So, any direction from which the Love wave comes in, it's going to record it. So the modern station, what it'll have, they'll always have two instruments like that—those horizontal pendulum instruments oriented at right angles to each other.

What about the Rayleigh wave, the up and down one? He didn't change the original instrument or anything. All he did was—

remember that piece of paper that was on the vertical part of the ring stand—all he did was he replaced that with another cylinder. And as the ring stand went up and down, the cylinder went up and down. It's rotating, it's translating—so, in other words, he gets another time recording for the Rayleigh wave. So, note, now, with these three instruments—two horizontal pendulum instruments at right angles to each other, and a vertical one—you can measure any shock wave coming in from any direction. You can tell when it arrives and when it stops. You can tell the change in wavelength during that— anything that has to do with time. Every modern seismic station is like that. There are three instruments like that. Usually a really modern station will have three sets of instruments like that that are really set for different frequencies, but we won't bother about talking about that. So, anyway, that's basically what the modern instrumentation looks like—except the only difference, like I say, is the modern instrument takes advantage of computers and all that kind of stuff. But the basic instruments are just the same.

Okay, now here's an important thing, though—we're talking time here. We want to know exactly what time this shock wave arrived by clock, see. Well, here's the problem. The original instruments probably used some kind of a clock mechanism where you set it, and every time it hit a second, it put a little tick on the recording like that—so they were timed. But here's the problem with using clocks like that. For example, if there are two of you in a room, and you say, "What time is it?" And you look at your watch, and you give a time, I'll guarantee you the person you're talking to will not have the same time on their watch. Why? It is pretty hard to have two timepieces exactly the same. So, what we needed, then, was some kind of a timing mechanism where every seismograph (maybe not in the world, but certainly in the immediate area—in the United States, anyway) is all ticking at the same time. And the way they do that, there's an atomic clock at Boulder, Colorado—that's where our big research center is for earthquakes. And there's an atomic clock there that sends a signal out by satellite, and every seismic station in this country—and I figure in much of the world—is tuned to that clock. So note: Everyone is ticking at exactly the same time. So now, you can compare a trace from Denver, Colorado, to one from Paris, France, or anywhere else you want, because they're all timing at the same time. So that's very, very important, as we'll see.

Okay, so let's talk about a typical seismogram—what the record looks like, this piece of paper. Now, of course, it's on a CRT screen—or actually stored in a computer. But anyway, what would it look like? Well, remember now, let's go back to our discussion of body waves and surface waves, and let's say we take just the simplest scenario. The focus is at the epicenter—they're both in the same place: We're talking a surface earthquake. Out from the focus go the body waves, and out from the epicenter go the surface waves. But the body waves are faster—remember, they're not moving the rock around; they're 24,000 miles an hour, so as far as getting to a distant station, the body waves will always arrive first, always arrive first. And then sometime after that, since they're slower, the surface waves will arrive. So that's going to be the fundamental part of this little drawing here is that the body waves arrive first—and then the surface waves.

Now, the body waves, though—remember our discussion of the body waves. You've got two kinds: p-waves—the compression, and s-waves—the shear waves. They're moving along the exact same path. Question: Are they going at the same speed? Now I wouldn't have asked the question if they were. No, they're not. One is faster than the other. Question: Which is the faster of the two? Well, it turns out that the p-wave is faster than the s-wave. Let me tell you how I've remembered that lo these many years. Think about those two waves. A shear wave, if the wave is moving away from you, let's say, the shear wave is moving things back and forth perpendicular to it. Remember? So note: Neither of those movements right there are doing anything for making the wave go in the direction of propagation. But on the other hand, the p-wave, now, since it's moving back and forth, and back and forth, in the direction of propagation, at least half the time energy is being spent moving in the direction of propagation. So I don't exactly know if that's why the velocities are different, but that's how I've remembered it lo these many years. So p-waves are all going to arrive first, then s-waves, and finally the surface waves are going to come in.

So you look at a typical trace. Here comes a trace along. The first one is the p-wave, the body p-wave. Remember, now, not much motion—so it's going to be very low in amplitude. And then some time right after that, there's going to be the s-wave come through. Again, there is not much motion because there's not much motion in the rocks. And then, finally, the great big one—the one you always you see sweeping across the chart—those are the surface waves that finally come in.

Okay, what do you want to tell? You've got a seismogram here. What do you want to tell from it? Well, one of the things you want to tell from it is where was the focus? Where was the epicenter? And then, how big was this earthquake? What was the Richter Scale reading, let's say, at the epicenter? Can you do that? Well, yes, you can. So here's the way it's done. Let's say we take, first of all, those body wave arrivals: the p-wave and the s-wave. Now here's the deal. Picture these as two racers—racer P and racer S—and just picture, now, a race between these two people running around a track, and we're going to make a plot now. We're going to plot time on the vertical axis versus distance on the horizontal axis. First of all, let's plot, say, the racer P. So all we have to do is watch him, and time him, and make a plot of time versus distance. And if you do that, as he races along—time versus distance, you get a line, now (just a simple straight line), which describes that performance of the racer P. Now let's put on top of that the performance of racer S. Now, remember, S is not as fast. So, for the same time interval, he will not have gone as far. And then, so, if you keep doing that for racer S, you'll get another curve—sort of diverging from 00 representing racer S. Note: The thing is, you've got two diverging curves.

What does it really tell you? Well, for example, let's say you're watching the race. What it really says, as time goes on—we're talking about the vertical component now—as time goes on, what it really says is the distance between those two racers will increase. And you see that. You just watch them run around the track, and you can see right off the bat the P racer pulls away from the S racer, and the gap between them in distance gets bigger and bigger. Well, that's what this plot says. So note: Besides that, it says that the further they run, the further they go, the time interval between them gets bigger and bigger. In other words, for any given distance you can look at this chart, and you can tell how far they would be apart in time.

Let's say, for example, this was a marathon, and you wanted to get to the start but you couldn't find out the time, and you didn't know where it started anyway. So you were just standing along the course some place. And the first runner came by, runner P, and you started a stopwatch, and then runner S came by, and you stopped it. So you know the time interval now, the time interval between these two racers. Note: If you have this plot, all you have to do is take that time interval now, find out where those two curves are separated by that time interval, drop right straight down to the bottom, and it says, "Oh yeah, the race started back about 5 miles ago. They've been running for 5 miles. That tells you how far back the race started. So note: By knowing the difference in time of arrivals of those two racers at your station, you can determine exactly where the race started.

So here's the way it works. You take this seismogram. You determine the P- and s-wave arrival times. There's a chart like that, and back in the old days, I guess, they had it hanging on the wall— now, of course, it's all in computer. You take that time, and you go to this chart either physically or in the computer, and it says, let's say, for your station, "Yeah, the earthquake was 2,000 miles away." So, here's what you do. You take a map out, you locate your station, and you draw around your station a circle 2,000 miles in radius. Now what you're saying is that earthquake occurred somewhere on that circle. Now you don't know where—but somewhere. But note: You've excluded everybody further out or closer in.

Then what do you do? You call another station, and the other station says, "Yes, we recorded that earthquake, too. And it was about 1,000 miles away from us." So what you do is then you find that station, the second station, and then you draw a circle around them—let's say 1,000 miles in radius. So, note, now, these two circles intersect at two places. Those two places are the only two places that it could possibly be. Because those two places are the only two places that are 2,000 miles from you and 1,000 miles from the second station— but you still have two. Then what do you? Pretty obvious, you call somebody else. And you say, "Did you record an earthquake?" "Yes." "How far away from you?" "About 500 miles." So you find them, and you draw a circle around them 500 miles in radius. And where all three intersect that's where it was. You have located now with three stations—and that's the point, you have to have the recordings from three stations to figure out where it was. The more you have, of course, the more accurate you can determine it.

Now here's another point. Think about this one: If those three circles intersect right on top of each other, meaning at a specific point, that means that's where the focus was—because, remember, that's what you're locating. That's where the focus was. It was a surface earthquake right at the surface. Remember, that's where most of them are. But what if the focus was actually at some depth. What if it was an intermediate focus earthquake below 40 miles or whatever? What would your plot look like? Think about that, now—what it would look like, rather than all three of those circles crossing at a point, they would cross sort-of in making sort-of a spherical triangle, you see, and the size of that spherical triangle is determined by how deep below the surface that focus really is. So the idea is that once you know the triangle dimensions, you can calculate, then, how far you would have to go down to see the point at which all three of them cross at a point. So you can determine, then, whether it's a shallow focus, or an intermediate focus, or a deep focus earthquake by simply calculating back from that spherical triangle—and that's how it's done.

How about the epicenter? Well the epicenter is always at the center of the triangle, regardless. So, now, simply with the recordings from three stations, you can locate the focus of the earthquake, and you've got the epicenter of the earthquake located. All right, what was the other thing we wanted to do? Well, what we wanted to do was figure out what was the Richter Scale reading at the epicenter? How much movement of the Earth was taking place at the epicenter? Well here's the deal. At the epicenter is where the maximum amount of movement was taking place, either back and forth or up and down. But here's the point: As you go away along the surface, the actual amplitude of the shock wave decreases in a regular fashion. By that I mean, probably, in a mathematical calculable fashion—away in all directions. So, as a result of that, out there someplace where you are, the actual movement of the Earth is much, much smaller, but you can measure it. That's what the seismograph does. What measures is that surface wave that comes through, that one that sweeps back and forth across.

Every instrument has its own calculations now—you can't apply this to everybody. But when you buy an instrument, here is what they tell you: Take that amplitude on the seismogram and measure it—probably in millimeters. And then they'll have a conversion chart that will say, "Once you know what the amplitude is on your seismogram, you can calculate exactly what the actual motion under your feet was." So note: If you can measure the actual motion out here, and if it decreases in regular fashion to that point, it would increase in regular fashion back to the epicenter. By regular fashion, again I mean mathematically. So here's the deal: If you want to know what the amplitude was back there at the epicenter, all you have to do is to take that motion here. Knowing how far away it was, you can calculate what that actual amplitude was at the epicenter. Once you know that, then it's a simple calculation from there to calculate what the Richter Scale reading is.

So here's the deal. Those are all relatively simple calculations, and any time you have simple calculations like that you can make a nomograph. What a *nomograph* is, it is simply, for example, here's a plot. And on one side you have a scale, where you take the P- and s-wave arrivals. Okay, you plot that—that's the distance, you see. On the other one, you measure the amplitude of your surface waves on your seismogram. And that, of course, is the actual movement there at your station. And you simply draw a line, and in between there's a scale that says Richter Scale reading, so you just read it right off. And so note the point: Any station at all can determine what the Richter Scale reading was. Any station can determine that. But determining where it was—that takes the records from at least three—and, of course, the more you have, the better off you're going to be and the more accurate your measurements are going to be.

One last comment, because they're always talking about predicting earthquakes. I'm going to tell you right here and now, you cannot predict an earthquake—they're like volcanic eruptions. We know they're going to happen—just like I predict that, you heard it here first, I predict that the next major earthquake along the San Andreas is going to be in the southern area around Los Angeles. Why? They haven't had one down there for over 150 years, you see. So anything that's been that long, it's got to happen down there. We just had one in 1906, you see, up in the northern end. So, I predict the next major earthquake is going to be in the Los Angeles area. When? I don't know. And see, there's the problem. Nobody can come up with an answer to the, "When's it going to be?" And unless you can predict pretty much right on the money, nobody's going to listen to you. Who's going to listen to you if you said, "I predict it's going to be somewhere within the next 50 years." What? In 50 years, I'll be the big seismic thing in the sky 50 years from now, you see. So, in answer to the question: "Will we ever be able to predict earthquakes? Will we ever be able to predict volcanic eruptions?"—my gut feeling, now, my gut feeling is: If we are, it's going to be a long,

long way into the future, long. And for the foreseeable future, I would say, "no."

Okay, so much for earthquakes and seismology.

Lecture Thirty-Three
The Formation of Mountains

Scope:

Mountains are of four types: *volcanic, domal, block-fault,* and *foldbelt*. Domal mountains are the simplest geologically and structurally and are categorized as *regional* or *local*. A good example of the latter is the area known as the Black Hills on the border of South Dakota and Wyoming. An example of block-fault mountains is the Basin and Range Province of Nevada. Foldbelt mountains, such as the Alps and the Himalayas, provide the most spectacular scenery and are caused by the most forceful of geological collisions—those at zones of subduction. Much of our current understanding of the origin of foldbelt mountains arose from studies of the Appalachian Mountains.

Outline

I. Although no absolute definition exists, to most geologists, the term *mountain* can be applied to any topographic feature that rises more than 1,000 feet above the surrounding terrain. There are four types of mountains: *volcanic, domal, block-fault,* and *foldbelt*.

   A. Volcanic mountains, as we have seen, are associated with three geologic scenarios: divergent plate margins, convergent plate margins, and hot spots.

   1. Mountains associated with divergent plate margins range from the thousands of cinder cones associated with rift zones, to Mt. Kilimanjaro located in the East African Rift Valley, to the oceanic ridges, which are, in fact, the most extensive mountain ranges on Earth, with a combined length of about 40,000 miles.

   2. The cones of the oceanic volcanoes of the oceanic ridges are very broad based, with gently sloping sides (shield volcanoes). The oceanic ridge in the Atlantic, for example, is roughly 2 miles high from its base but 1,000–1,500 miles wide. Given that the Atlantic itself is only about 3,000 miles across, the oceanic ridge occupies one-third to one-half of the ocean floor.

3. Scenically, the most impressive volcanic mountains are the island-arc and continental-arc volcanic mountain chains associated with the convergent plate margins, as we have already discussed.

4. An example of an oceanic ridge rising over a hot spot above the ocean surface is Iceland. Part of the rift valley associated with the oceanic ridge can be seen running through the center of Iceland.

B. Although the epeirogenic (vertical) forces that create them are perhaps the most difficult to explain, domal mountains are the simplest both geologically and structurally of all the various kinds of mountains.

1. The vertical forces responsible for domal mountains originate beneath continental crust far from any plate boundary. The best explanation for epeirogenic forces is heat that accumulates under the continental crust, causing the rocks to expand. The subsequent decrease in density and increase in buoyancy causes the hot rocks to rise and the overlying crust to dome.

2. The resultant doming can be of either a *local* or *regional* type.

3. An example of regional doming is the uplift of the continental crust in the Colorado Plateau.

C. The rocks underlying the Basin and Range portion of the Colorado uplift (situated in Nevada) are thinner than under the Colorado Plateau and, subsequently, weaker. Although the rocks of the Colorado Plateau were little affected by the tensional forces that developed, the rocks of the Basin and Range were broken by many parallel north-south–trending normal faults. The result of the normal faulting was the creation of block-fault mountains throughout the region.

1. Block-faulting occurs under two scenarios. In one case, the faults are parallel and dip in the same direction, resulting in a rotation of the block between the faults and forming a mountain ridge along one edge of the block and a down-thrown basin along the other.

2. In the second scenario, the parallel faults alternate in dip direction, resulting in an up-thrown mountain range bordered by fault scarps on both sides, a relatively flat

summit, and a down-thrown block forming the adjoining basins.

- **D.** An excellent example of local doming is the area on the South Dakota/Wyoming border known as the Black Hills. This is a north-south–trending dome about 50 miles wide and 100–150 miles long that rises to just over 7,000 feet above sea level.
    1. We do not know if heat caused this relatively small area to dome, but in the process of uplifting, the sedimentary rock that once covered the area was stripped away, exposing a core of granitic rocks.
    2. During the Archean period, 1.5 billion years ago, the rocks at the core of the Black Hills were formed through hydrothermal metamorphism and injected with gold.
    3. The Black Hills were sacred to the Sioux Nation but were overrun by white prospectors in the late 1800s. All gold produced from the Black Hills today is restricted to rocks that go back to the Archean age.

II. Most foldbelt mountains are located near the edges of continents, with the core (a complex mixture of igneous and metamorphic rock) located seaward and the folded *sedimentary basin*, landward.

- **A.** Much of our current understanding of the origin of foldbelt mountains arose from studies that began in the mid-1800s by an American paleontologist, James Hall, who was investigating the section of sedimentary rocks associated with what is now called the Valley and Ridge Province of the Appalachian Physiographic Provinces.
- **B.** Hall observed that while most sedimentary rocks were of shallow marine origin, the sedimentary rocks associated with the Appalachians were very thick.
- **C.** Geologists were agreed that the marine sedimentary rocks formed from the sediments that accumulated on the continental shelf with an average depth of only about 600 feet. Hall's main problem was to explain how tens of thousands of feet of sediments could accumulate in a part of the ocean that was, at most, only 600 feet deep.
- **D.** Hall's conclusion was that the surface of the continental shelf continuously down-warped under the weight of the

sediments, forming a giant syncline. A contemporary, James Dana, called the structure a *geosyncline*.

E. With the advent of the theory of plate tectonics, we now know that a wedge of sediment called a *geocline* begins to accumulate along the margin of newly formed continents and continues to grow seaward for the lifetime of the ocean. The result is an ever-thickening sediment wedge, while a shallow marine environment is maintained over the continental shelf.

F. A continent-continent collision compresses the geocline, folding it to ultimately become a range of foldbelt mountains.

G. All the great mountains of the world are foldbelt mountains—the Alps, the Himalayas, and the Appalachians, for example.

H. It is the force of a collision at the zone of subduction that makes the folds that become foldbelt mountains.

Recommended Reading:

Bloom, A. L., *Geomorphology: A Systematic Analysis of Late Cenozoic Landforms.*

Questions to Consider:

1. Why are most of Earth's major mountain ranges located along the margins of continents?

2. What is the most logical source of energy for epeirogenic forces?

Lecture Thirty-Three—Transcript
The Formation of Mountains

The topic is mountains. As a teacher, I think of all the lectures we've had in this series, this is the one that probably is most frustrating for me. I mean, we're going to talk about four of the great mountain types of the world, and there have been books written on each one of them. So, obviously, we're simply going to touch the surface, but I think I can give you a feeling for what the different kinds are, and that's what my objective here is. So let's just start talking about the four.

First of all, what is a mountain? I better define it for you. It depends. For example, there's a definition that I read one time that said: "A *mountain* is a topographic high, significantly higher than the surrounding terrain." Question: What is significant? Well, it really didn't say. So it's just this "topographic feature significantly higher than the surrounding terrain," which brings up a field trip I was on one time. I think we were driving down through the Carolinas, and we're out on the coastal plane now. You have to picture, now, this is perfectly flat: looks like a pancake. And so we're driving along, and here the sign appears, "Visit Mount So-and-So Overlook, 20 miles." And I looked around, and you couldn't even see anything—I mean, it's flat as a pancake. So we're driving along, and we see 15 miles. Pretty soon a sign shows up, "Entrance to Mount So-and-So." So we drive into this thing just to see what it's like. I mean it had to be no higher than 300 feet above the ground, the surface. I mean it was a hill, and yet it was called Mount So-and-So. Why? Well, I guess to the people living in the area, it was the highest point around, so I guess it was sort of an overlook. So the point is, it just has to be in the eyes of the beholder, I guess. I suppose somebody probably got a nosebleed walking up there, but 300 feet—we would hardly call that a mountain. I guess the definition that most geologists would go by is that a *mountain* is any topographic feature higher than 1,000 feet around the surrounding terrain. So, we put sort of a limit on it. Anything over 1,000 feet would be a mountain, technically, and anything under that would simply be a hill.

A little bit of trivia for you I might throw out. In Nepal, we're talking the Himalaya now, in Nepal there's a law that says in order to use the word *mountain* to describe something, the summit has to be greater than 26,000 feet above sea level. Mt. Everest is only 29,000, so

©2006 The Teaching Company Limited Partnership

they're really pretty particular over there with what they call "mountains."

Okay, kinds of mountains. There are four basic kinds of mountains: We're talking *volcanic mountains*, we're talking *block-fault mountains*, we're talking *domal mountains*, and the big guys that we'll see at the end are called *foldbelt mountains*. Let's talk about the volcanic first. Actually, we've been talking about these a lot. These are associated with the plate margins. So, if we think about the zones of subduction, for example. Major mountains of the world would be the arc volcanoes. We're talking about *continental-arc* volcanoes like the Andes. We're talking *island-arc* volcanoes like the Aleutian Islands and the Japanese Islands. So, we're talking major, major mountains here, and I'm not sure I really have anything to add to that. I think you understand, now, how they form from those andesitic magmas along the zones of subduction. But they are indeed major, major mountains.

Let's talk a little bit about the *divergent plate margins*. We're talking rift zones, rift valley—and finally, of course, the oceanic ridge. Let's talk a little bit about the rift zone. For example, if you went into a rift zone, would you expect to see any mountains? Well, remember, we talked about some things that formed in rift zones. One of them were these cinder cones—remember, these are basaltic eruptions—and, as a result, whenever you have a basaltic eruption, it could possibly have enough gas in it when it reaches the surface to blow the molten rock up into the air—maybe 1,000 feet, maybe 2,000 feet at the most. And as it breaks up into little pieces and falls solid as cinders, you have this cinder cone pile up around the vent. How high do they get? Well, most of the ones I've seen probably were less than 1,000 feet—so, you see, they would qualify as hills, perhaps, but not as mountains. But there are some greater than that, there are some that would be over 1,000 feet—so it is conceivable that if you went into a rift a zone, you could find topographic highs that are greater than 1,000 feet above the surrounding terrain. So, yeah, you could have mountains like that: cinder cones in rift zones.

How about the rift valleys? Well, thinking, now, about the Great Rift Valley of Africa—that's the one that we have today—we're talking sort of big-time volcanic activity in the great valleys. You've got lots and lots of lava being spewed out. We have lots and lots of the hot springs and all that. But we also have volcanoes—honest-to-God volcanoes—now. For example, we have Mt. Kilimanjaro. You've all heard of Mt. Kilimanjaro. Mt. Kilimanjaro rises, I believe, it's about 19,000 feet above sea level. That's a pretty good size volcano. Mt. Kenya is another one. So, in a scenario like that: Yes, you could and indeed do have mountains created within the rift valleys.

But let's talk about the big guy now. Let's go out in the ocean, and rip those apart, and talk a little bit about that oceanic ridge. The interesting thing about the oceanic ridge is this, of course, would be—we've said it before—the biggest mountain range in the world in terms of length. We're talking a total of 40,000 miles of these things all connected together—one in every ocean. And the problem at first when students start reading about, or hearing about, oceanic ridges—and I think a lot of the problem is simply in the instructors, like me, who describe these things as long mountain ranges—but they get the feeling and the idea that they're steep on the side just like a typical mountain range on land: Figure it looks like the Rockies, the Northern Rockies. No, that's not quite it. Remember now, what we're talking about here, building from the ocean floor, is basaltic eruptions. Now, think of the shield volcanoes building over a hot spot for a moment: This thing erupted to the surface of the ocean, and then spread out. And then the next eruption on top of that spread out. And you end up with this cone that's not really very high, but it's very, very broad across the base. Why? Well, you can't pile liquids up very high. Liquids just won't pile very high. So here's—now, my colleagues would probably cringe at hearing me say this—but here's the picture I would have you have for what the oceanic ridge really is. I would sort of picture it as an infinite number, now, of shield volcanoes—just all the length of the ocean bottom. And I think the picture, then, you have is a mountain range, note: with very gently sloping sides up to the summit of the ocean ridge. Well, you look at the typical oceanic ridge, it's rising from the ocean floor—which before it was built on was probably maybe 10,000 to 12,000 feet deep—and then you're building this ridge up to 1,000 feet of the surface. So, we're talking about a ridge that would have above its base maybe two miles, okay, 10,000 feet, roughly two miles.

But if it's two miles high—thinking, now, of the shield volcano—the width is going to be enormous. Well, it is if you look, for example, at the oceanic ridge in the Atlantic, we're talking about a ridge that's say roughly two miles high from its base, but the width of it is maybe 1,000 or 1,500 miles wide. So think about that now. We're talking about the ocean itself is only 3,000 miles across—so even at 1,000 miles across its base, we're talking about the oceanic ridge occupying at least a third to a half of the ocean bottom. And so all of a sudden the picture you have, then, of what this really looks like is quite a bit different—it's quite a bit different. And so it's a very gently sloping kind of a mountain range.

And here's the other thing we were talking about: Most of the time it's submarine, and that's, of course, the reason why we never knew they were there because no one had ever seen one before, until we finally understood plate tectonics. But here we have Iceland. Here's a question for you: Why is Iceland there? Why is that part, that small portion of the North Atlantic oceanic ridge, why is it tall enough to poke its head above water? Well, there's a reason for it, and the reason for it is because, just fortuitously, underneath the oceanic ridge, there is located a hot spot. This is one of the hundred or so active hot spots on Earth. And so now, you have a hot spot underneath the oceanic ridge, generating its own basaltic magmas, you see. So here's the point. You have the basaltic magma that's normally coming to the surface along the summit of the ridge itself, building it up toward sea level. But then you have additional basaltic magmas coming up from the hot spot adding to that. And as a result, this part of the ridge, then, builds up above the ocean level, and we have the island of Iceland.

And if you go to Iceland, remember now, there's actually a rift valley right down the summit of all these oceanic ridges as they continue to be pulled apart, you see—and that's where all the active volcanism is going on. Well, if you go to the island of Iceland, you'll actually see part of that down-drop block of the so-called *rift valley* right through the island of Iceland. So, anyway, that's the reason why it's there. So, a little bit different story now, or a little bit different picture than you might have of what these oceanic ridges look like.

Okay, the hot spots, out in the ocean again, and I really don't have anything to add to that. You already know what they are—we're talking possibly building up sea mounts and breaking through to cause volcanic islands like the Hawaiian Islands, and I really don't have anything more to add to that one.

So, let's move on and talk a little bit about block-fault mountains. Now, again, we've mentioned these in the past, but let's sort of review what this is all about. We've mentioned the fact that starting about 10 million years ago there was a huge area in the Southwest that was uplifted—we call that *regional doming*. So the whole area was uplifted about 10,000 feet, and the question was: Why? Well, we really don't know. What we do know is it seems to have absolutely nothing to do whatsoever with plate tectonics. And that's one of our problems, of course—we always call upon plate tectonics, but now, we're not going to get an answer from that. So what would cause such an uplift, such a doming over a large area like that? Well, you know, I've read a lot about that, and it seems that one thing keeps coming up. And the idea is that heat accumulates underneath this portion of the continental crust. And as the heat accumulates, the rocks expand. And as the rocks expand, the density goes down, and they become more buoyant. So the picture is that it's the buoyancy of these hot rocks—not necessarily molten now, but hot rocks—that causes the entire uplift. Is that the way it happened? Well, I don't know—it's scientifically sound, and it seems to explain what we see. And that's all the theory has to do. The only thing a theory has to be is scientifically sound—and I see nothing wrong with the science of that particular explanation—and it has to explain what you see, and it does.

The question is: Why would the heat concentrate under the continental mass more so than anywhere else? Well, again, I'm not really sure why, but let me just pose something. This is just a theory that I'm going to throw out on my own, I guess. Let's say, for example, the Earth—there is heat coming to the surface of the Earth everywhere. I mean, for example, we've got a molten core down there, but it's cooling off. So, heat is being conducted through the Earth from the core to the surface to radiate out into space. And then, most people don't realize this, but there's a lot of heat generated within Earth from radioactive breakdown of radioactive elements, and that heat's coming to the surface, too. So a question I would pose for you: Let's say, we are going to compare, now, the ability of the heat to be transmitted, conducted through, let's say, the oceanic crust—just the crust now—as opposed to the continental crust. Well, here you have the oceanic crust, what is it? The average is about 5 miles thick, basaltic stuff. But you see, the continental crust is a lot thicker than that, a lot thicker: tens of miles, maybe 50 to 60 miles

©2006 The Teaching Company Limited Partnership

thick in places—maybe more than that. So here's the question I would have: If heat is rising under both of those, which one of those two layers, do you think, would conduct heat to the surface and then radiate it into space more efficiently? Well, I think you'd say the thinner one. Yeah, I would say the same thing. So, here's this very, very thick mass of granitic rock. Here comes the heat up—well, that thick mass of granitic rock could act like an insulator. And, as a result, the heat isn't going to be conducted so readily to the surface. Therefore, it might accumulate. Therefore, it might expand the rocks, and so result in the buoyancy that causes this uplift.

Regardless of what it was, I don't know, but in any case, the whole area was uplifted. And the two areas we've talked about being created as a result of that: the Colorado Plateau is one of them, and right next door, remember—the Basin and Range, the Basin and Range Province. Now, the difference between the two—as far as we can tell—the difference is that the rocks under the Colorado Plateau were thick enough that during this uplift there was no deformation to them, no breaking. Tensional forces were being generated within them because that's what happens when you have this regional uplift. But they're thick enough and strong enough that there's no breaking going on. But if we move over and look at that Basin and Range Province—and we're really dealing, now, largely with the state of Nevada—the rocks apparently there are thinner. Thinner means weaker. Weaker means under the tensional forces—same tensional forces now—but the rocks start to break. Well, under tensional forces, you remember, we're going to have domal faults. So here's the scenario: The scenario within the Basin and Range, the two scenarios are the generation of high-angle normal faults. Tensional, you see, that's what happens under tension.

So, the first scenario is: All the faults basically dip in the same direction—so if you can picture, let's say, you're looking north. You're in the state of Nevada, and you have all the faults, just for our little description, let's say they're all dipping to the east, okay. What's going to happen between adjacent faults is the block is going to sort of rotate. So what you're going to get now—they're all going to strike north. Now, that's the thing to point out: They always strike north. So, here's what you're going to have. You're going to have a mountain ridge—one side of which is going to be a fault scarp, that's where the actual break occurred. The fault scarp in the ridge is going to be due north-south—that's going to be the orientation. The other side is going to be gently sloping layers of sedimentary rock that slope off to the fault scarp on the next block. And then, over time, erosion of those two ridgelines is going to dump material into that basin. And then we're going to go through what we talked about before: alluvial fans, and bajadas, and the bolson, and all that to fill in that valley. So, that would be one scenario. Those would be *block-fault mountains*. That's one scenario that it could form. But note: In any case, north-south trending, faults on one side slipping off into the fault on the next side.

The other scenario is where they alternate: east, west, east, west. So, if you can imagine again, looking north, and how we have alternate between eastward-dipping fault and a westward, eastward-dipping fault, and they alternate like that. Then, picture what's going to happen. What's going to happen is that hanging-wall block is going to fall down relative to the foot-wall block, which is going to go up. So now, we have ridges, again, north-south trending ridges—that's the strike. But now, we're going to have—each ridge is going to be bounded on both sides, on the east and on the west, by a fault scarp. The top is going to be flat. The rocks in the block are going to be horizontal because there was no tilting, you see. And then, once again, the next one over is going to erode just like this one, and all the sediment is going to be fed into that down-faulted block, and fill it in with alluvial fans, and bajadas, and that whole bit again. So again, we have again, north-south trending block-fault mountains—and that's what characterizes the Basin and Range. And that probably is the very, very best illustration of block-fault mountains that I've ever seen anywhere in the world. So, anyway, there are your block-fault mountains.

Now, let's go on to talk about doming again. And this time, what I want to talk about is more *local doming* rather than that big, *regional doming*, because I want to introduce to you a place where, perhaps, you've been. And hopefully, if you haven't, you will go after watching this course. But, anyway, the place I'm thinking about is the Black Hills. The Black Hills is a localized dome. It's a dome. It's about 150 miles long, and it's about 50 miles wide. It sits down there in that southwestern corner of South Dakota, and it's out in the middle of nowhere. Around it you're talking about the Great Plains now, and all of a sudden, here's this mountain range that pops up. What caused it to rise? What was the force that caused this doming?

Well, this is one we really argue about. Some people say, "Well, it's the same heat business we talked about before." I'm not sure that's true. I mean we're talking about a very small portion, you see, of the total crust of the Earth there. Another theory says that it's the result of compression from the west. See about the same time this dome was piled up, the Rocky Mountains were forming over to the west. So somebody believes that it's all part of the compressional forces that created the Rocky Mountains. I really don't know—it may be.

But anyway, let's go back to this dome. As the dome was uplifted, what we're actually uplifting is the core of the continent itself, the granitic core. And then what happened, of course, the sedimentary rock that once covered this is largely stripped away, exposing now, in the center of the Black Hills, this crystalline core made up of granitic rocks, and metamorphic rocks, and things like that. And then the sedimentary rocks, of course, dip away in all directions—those would be the monoclinal folds we talked about.

Now, I want to bring this one up because every time I have the opportunity in my class, I always bring up history. If I can find someplace where geology was involved in the history of a region, of a place, I always do it because I think it's important to set geology into the scene. There are things that happen in our historical background that are directly controlled by the geology of the area, and here's a good example: these Black Hills. These Black Hills were sacred to the Sioux Nation. Now, the Sioux Nation was there long before anybody ever headed in this direction from Europe. I don't know how long the Sioux Nation has been in that area, but it was long before we showed up on the scene. So, here's the Sioux Nation. They considered this sacred—so sacred, this was the place of their gods. The only people who were allowed to go into the Black Hills were medicine men and then only to bury their dead chieftains. So, anyway, this was a very, very sacred place.

And that's the way it was for a long time until we started showing up. We started showing up in that part of the world what—maybe the early 1800s: Remember the settlers moving into the Great Plains. And the interesting thing is, when they moved in, someone made a discovery. They made a discovery that in the streams draining the Black Hills, coming out of the Black Hills, there was gold. Now, gold turns people crazy, and that's all there is to it. Gold was in these streams. Now, the miners knew enough about gold and how it occurred to know that if the gold is in these streams, it's coming from the core of the Black Hills. Now, here's a little point for you: All the gold produced in the world today—and I don't care where you go—all the gold produced in the world today pretty much is restricted at the source to rocks that are about 1.5 to 1.6 billion years ago. We call them the *Archean*. That's the rocks at the core of the Black Hills. During that period of time 1.5 billion years ago, hydrothermal metamorphism, remember that, with things in it that the rocks didn't need to make minerals, like gold, was injected into the rocks and changed the rocks—metamorphosed them and emplaced things like gold. That's where the gold around the world is. That's where the gold was here, too—it was in the core. So, anyway, I'm sure there were people who went into the Black Hills trying to find some of that stuff. Of course, the Sioux people found them and wiped them out because they were not allowed in there.

Interestingly enough, the federal government made a treaty with the Indians—let's see, this would have been 1868—that this was part of their nation, we'll never go in there, you don't have to worry, it's yours. We'll never allow anybody in there. But still, interestingly enough, they wanted to know, "Is there gold in those hills?" What they did, they hired a bunch of prospectors to go in, of course, and the prospectors said, "No, we're not going to do that: The Sioux will wipe us out." So they sent along some protection, and you know who they sent? George Armstrong Custer and the 7th Calvary. So he took them in there, and they were only supposed to look around and see if there was gold. Once George got in there he got kind of greedy, and he started looking for gold, and I guess he found some. But he didn't find as much as he was supposed to, I guess, so in order to save face, he sort of made it public through the press that, "Yeah, there's a lot of gold in there." And then, of course, all the prospectors were moving in—forget about the treaty. The Homestake Mine, for example, was established in 1876, and that mine, I do believe, is still the largest producer of gold in this country from the Home State Mine in the Black Hills. And then, in 1877, the federal government said, "Remember that treaty we had with you guys? Forget it. Get out, we're going to take over the Black Hills again." So, anyway, there's a little bit of history for you—not very pleasant but, nevertheless, some history. That's also the place where Mt. Rushmore is with all the faces—you've got to see those.

Okay, foldbelt. These are the great mountains of the world, the *foldbelt mountains.* Now, here's the characteristic of all foldbelt mountains. There are two components to them: side-by-side, almost always paralleling the edge of the continent, always paralleling it. The first one is a very complex mixture of igneous rocks, metamorphic rocks, volcanic rocks—and it forms this complex usually right at the very margin of the continent. And then, inland from that, that there's another component—there's a *sedimentary basin,* and that's the folded part. These rocks are folded. So, every foldbelt mountain looks like that: a complex component along the edge of the continent, and then, inland, this folded mass of sedimentary rocks. Now, the interesting thing about our understanding of this really goes back, this would be about in the middle 1800s.

The first person to actually study foldbelt mountains in any systematic way was an American geologist by the name of James Hall. The time would have been, I think, around 1857. Hall actually worked for the New York Geological Survey, and he was studying the Appalachians. The Appalachians have to be the most widely studied single mountain range in the world. Why? You can cross the whole mountain range in only about four or five hours, you see—so it's easy to get around. But anyway, he was in there studying the rocks within the Appalachian Mountains themselves—we talked about the folded Appalachians. He made an amazing discovery. He discovered that the total thickness, now, of sedimentary rock within the folded Appalachians was many, many times greater than the total thickness of sedimentary rocks in the interior of the continent, let's say, in the Mississippi Valley. When I say "total thickness" I mean above the bedrock, the granitic bedrock. The question is: How could you explain that? Well, these rocks, for the most part, were marine in origin because they had the fossils in them. That way we knew that they formed off shore, and they knew the continent went out, so that offshore area we called the continental shelf before it dropped off into the deep. That's where the sediment was being poured out there; that's where the sedimentary rocks were being formed. But here's the problem: That area out there, the continental shelf, averages about maybe 100 miles wide, but out at the outer edge before it drops off into the deep, it's only, on the average, 600 feet deep. How could you possibly accumulate tens of thousands of feet of rock in an ocean that's only 600 feet deep?

So he came up with this idea. He pictured that what was happening as all those sediments were being poured out there, the surface of the continental shelf was being bowed down into a syncline, you see, and the idea was sort of like dumping dirt into a rubber bag. You keep dumping it in: The level of the dirt at the stop stays the same, but the bottom of the bag keeps falling out. And you ended up bowing this down and accumulating thousands and thousands of feet. Well, it was a syncline, okay, of gigantic proportions, and so he called it a *geosyncline*.

Well, that was the picture we had, and we used that as an explanation for where all of these tens of thousands of sedimentary rocks came from until plate tectonics came onto the scene. Once plate tectonics came onto the scene, we have, now, a little bit different picture. Picture now, for example, a continent breaking up, rift zone—we're in the rift valley stage. Picture the rift valley now. Remember the drawings we always show—just great normal faults along the edge of the rift valley, downfall of blocks forming the valley itself. Then what we're going to do eventually, we're going to take the valley, and that's where the split's going to occur, after it goes through the linear ocean. And so, one half of the valley goes left with one part of the continent, and the other goes right with the other one. And so, now, we have the edge of the continent, now, in an opening ocean. As it begins to open, on the edge of the continent are these high-angle normal faults making sort of a step-stair kind of thing down into the ocean deep. Now, right from the very beginning, sediments are coming off the land, being carried out into the ocean by currents of the ocean. And just picture, now, that sediment sort of being carried out, and then sort of cascading down over the edge of those blocked ends—just like the sort of stuff cascading down a stairway. And picture that now going on for 200 million years—that's what's happening in the Atlantic. Eventually you're going to get this huge wedge, now, of sedimentary rock that's going to be able to create tens of thousands of feet of sediments. Well, we can't call it a geosyncline anymore because there's no syncline to it. So, what we call that is a *geocline*, so that's the new picture of what it was like.

Well here, now, we have the geocline, tens of thousands of feet, perhaps, of sediment turned into sedimentary rock. How do you form these mountains then? Well, we're going to talk about that in some detail in the next lecture. But picture, now, a continental collision between one continent and another. Sooner or later, the continents

©2006 The Teaching Company Limited Partnership

are going to get together, and all of a sudden you've got this collision at the zone of subduction. The zone of subduction, now, you have all this material coming up—the granitic rocks, the metamorphic rocks, the volcanic rocks. And all the while what's happening back there in that geocline? Well, these tremendous compressive forces are simply taking it and squeezing it under compression. And note what's going to happen: Folds are going to start to form. And remember our discussion of folds—the different kinds of folds—over there closest to the point of collision, you're going to have the *recumbent folds.* And then as we get further away from it, they're going to turn into *overturned folds,* and then they're going to turn into *asymmetric folds,* and they're going to turn into *symmetric high amplitude folds,* and finally, they're going to turn into *low amplitude symmetrical folds.* So, that's the folded part. So, there's your real picture of a foldbelt mountain range, then. You have this complex unit along the coastline resulting from the collision of continents—which we'll talk about in detail next time—and then the folded sediments that once accumulated in that so-called geocline.

All the great mountains of the world look like that. And, of course, the Appalachians look like that, and the Alps look like that, the Himalaya; all the great mountains of the world are examples of foldbelt mountains. The only difference between one foldbelt mountain and the other is going to be in exactly the way that compressive force takes place, and that is going to be the topic of the next lecture—namely what we call *orogenic processes. Orogeny* is the word, that's mountain building—and we're going to find out that there are only three ways that mountains can be really created like that, and that's the topic of the next lecture.

Lecture Thirty-Four
Orogenic Styles

Scope:

Foldbelt mountains are formed through various types of collision. The ocean-continent type begins with the formation of a geocline along the coastal margin of a continent. An accretionary wedge comes to the ocean surface along the zone of subduction and is lifted to form a coastal mountain range. The deformation of the sedimentary geocline also ultimately contributes to the formation of mountains. The Andes are an example of this type of formation. The ocean-island arc-continent collision begins with a zone of subduction that forms further offshore than the one that ultimately produced the ocean-continent collision. The end result is an island-arc chain of volcanic islands, such as the Japanese Islands. Some of the most impressive mountains are the result of a continent-continent collision, as, for example, when India collided with Asia, producing the Himalayas.

Outline

I.   The term *orogeny* refers to the processes by which foldbelt mountains form, all of which involve massive, *horizontal* compression. (*Epeirogeny* is the process of *vertical* compression.) Foldbelt mountains form under three basic convergent scenarios: ocean-continent collisions, ocean-island arc-continent collisions, and continent-continent collisions.

   A. Foldbelt mountains have two parallel components, a complex core made up of a mixture of igneous and metamorphic rocks and a zone of folded and faulted sedimentary rocks.

   B. The ocean-continent collision begins with the formation of a geocline along the margin of a continent adjoining an opening ocean.

      1. The coastlines of the supercontinent of Pangea would have been the sites of geoclines, accumulating sediment from the interior of the vast supercontinent. When Pangea broke up about 200 million years ago, the new continents of South and North America began moving

westward, forming zones of subduction along their western margins as the oceanic lithosphere plunged below the continental lithosphere.

2. Some of the stress along the zone of subduction was relieved by the formation of thrust faults that brought mixtures of igneous rocks, metamorphic rocks, and meta-sediments to the ocean surface along the zone of subduction as an accretionary wedge. The mixture of rock types within the accretionary wedge is called a *melange.*

3. The descending plate was subjected to increasing temperatures and pressure and converted into metamorphic rock. At great depths, magmas began to form, as seawater and water provided from the dehydration of hydrous minerals initiated the melting of existing rocks.

4. Continued formation of thrust faults eventually lifted the accretionary wedge to form a coastal mountain range. As deformation continued, andesitic magmas began erupting to the surface (in stratovolcanoes), creating a continental-arc mountain range. Simultaneously, massive volumes of granitic magma were intruded into the edge of the continent.

5. While these events were shaping the edge of the new continent, the sediments that had previously accumulated in the geocline were being deformed by compressive forces into folds, as we discussed earlier. The axes of the folds paralleled the continental margin, with asymmetric folds forming nearest the continental margin and becoming more symmetrical inland.

6. With time, the folded rocks nearest the continental margin began to resist further folding and broke along thrust faults that drove rocks inland. This sequence of events resulted in the Andes Mountains.

C. The early events of the ocean-island arc-continent collision are the same as those described for the ocean-continent collision. The difference in this scenario is that the zone of subduction forms further offshore.

1. Once again, an accretionary wedge forms seaward of the island arc. As andesitic magmas continue to erupt to the

surface, adding to the volcanic mountain chain, granitic magmas begin to intrude into the cores of the islands, progressively thickening the mass of the islands and resulting in the creation of an island-arc chain of volcanic islands, such as the Aleutian Islands.

2. As this process continues, granitic magma begins to rise to the surface, lifting the chain of islands, emplacing itself in the mass of volcanic rocks, freezing, and forming batholiths. This creates the complex core of volcanic islands found, for example, in the Japanese Islands.

3. A back-arc basin forms between the island arc and the continent that accumulates sediments from both the island and the land side, adding to the geoclinal sediments already present. In some cases, rifting within the back-arc basin results in the formation of a marginal sea, such as the Sea of Japan.

4. As compressive forces continue, the sediments within the back-arc basin or marginal sea are folded, faulted, and thrust up onto the continental margin in the form of stacked-thrust sheets of sedimentary rocks.

5. Through this process, the Japanese Islands will eventually be forced landward. The sediments in the basin will be folded and thrust up on the edge of the Asian continent and come to resemble the Andes Mountains in South America.

II. Some of the truly impressive mountains of the world are examples of continent-continent collisions.

   A. To illustrate the continent-continent collision, we return to the breakup of Pangea, when a small fragment that was to become India headed northward. India had its own geocline, out in front, and was heading toward Asia.

      1. The ocean bottom was being subducted off the coast of Asia. On the Asian continent, an accretionary wedge rose high above the ocean. Between the volcanic-arc complex and the accretionary wedge was a basin, known as a *fore-arc basin*, which was accumulating sediment.

      2. When India's geocline ran into the accretionary wedge of Asia, India's geocline was thrust southward and folded into a foldbelt mountain range. The fore-arc basin

was thrust northward on top of Asia, resulting in another foldbelt mountain range. The continental lithosphere of India was low-density rock, which uplifted as the Himalayas were formed. In fact, the Himalayas are still rising because of the buoyancy of that portion of the lithosphere. All this happened about 45 million years ago.

B. Another example of a continent-continent collision occurred about 350 million years ago when the continents of Laurentia (North America plus Greenland) and Gondwana (primarily Africa) collided, contributing to the formation of the supercontinent of Pangea, with a central, highly deformed core and folded mountains of sedimentary rocks on the west and east sides. The picture would have been similar to the Himalayas.

    1. When Pangea began to break up about 200 million years ago, the break occurred along the central core of the mountain range, with one-half of its foldbelt mountains going westward with the newly formed North American continent and the other half, with its foldbelt mountains, going eastward with the newly formed continent of Africa.

    2. Perhaps 100 million years later, any surface expression of those mountains would have eroded away, very close to sea level. However, about 60 million years ago, the entire eastern margin of North America, from the Mississippi to the outer edge of the continental shelf, was uplifted in a broad arch about 6,000 feet. Streams were rejuvenated, and a new topography resulted in the Appalachians.

    3. The basic rock structures of the Appalachians remained as they were when they were created at the time the continents of Gondwana and Laurentia collided. This crystalline core is visible in the Piedmont.

C. The other half of the Appalachians—broken off when Pangea split up—became the Atlas Mountains in Africa.

III. Future mountain building will occur if Africa runs into Europe and, after that, if Australia collides with China.

A. The bottom of the Mediterranean Sea is being consumed by a zone of subduction, which means that Africa is moving toward Europe. If the continents collide, the resulting mountain range will be equal in grandeur to the Himalayas.

B. In the same way, the Indonesian zone of subduction is drawing Australia closer to China; the two may collide in the far distant future.

Recommended Reading:

Bloom, A. L., *Geomorphology: A Systematic Analysis of Late Cenozoic Landforms*.

Questions to Consider:

1. In what ways do orogenic and epeirogenic mountain-building forces differ?

2. In what ways do mountains created by continent-continent collisions differ from those formed by ocean-continent or ocean-island arc-continent collisions?

Lecture Thirty-Four—Transcript
Orogenic Styles

I want to conclude our discussion of mountain building with the introduction of something we call *orogenic styles*, ways in which the mountains are created. Remember, now, what an orogeny is: An *orogeny* is a mountain-building episode. But the significance of the orogeny is we're dealing here with massive horizontal compression. That's the big difference, as opposed to *epeirogeny*, which was the vertical—we're talking about massive horizontal compression.

Now, I would ask you the question: Where on earth would you expect to find the maximum horizontal compressive forces? Well, I think you know now where it is. It's the zones of subduction. There's no place on earth you're going to have any more compressive forces than that. This is the biggest head-on collision in the world we're talking about here. And the other thing we're going to be talking about in these orogenic styles is the creation of those so-called *foldbelt mountains*. Remember, the great mountains of the world are foldbelt mountains, and they consist of those two parallel components: one, a complex core, which is made up of sort of a mixture of igneous rocks, and metamorphic rocks, and volcanic rocks; and then the other part is a parallel zone of folded and faulted sedimentary rocks. So that's what we're going to be driving at.

Okay, the three styles we're going to talk about are: *ocean-continent, ocean-island arc-continent*—and then, finally, *continent-continent*. So, let's think about the ocean continent first. And to set the scene for this, let's go back and look at Pangea before she broke up. Now, in particular, what I want you to picture is South America, the portion we're going to call South America. Before Pangea broke up, all along the edge of what is now South America there had formed a *geocline*: Remember, now, the geocline is this thick stack of sedimentary rocks that forms out toward the edge of the continent. Now, we're going to break up Pangea—200 million years ago—and then South America is going to start moving westward, and we're going to start creating, then, the Atlantic Ocean, of course. But here in the Pacific, now, something's going to happen. Here you have, basically, South America heading west. But there's an ocean basin there, you see, so it runs into this ocean basin, and we start to develop those compressive forces.

So now, let's watch the sequence of events now, fingers together, compressive forces. Remember, you push the fingers together—remember, we were sort of down-warping and down-warping. What we're creating here, of course, is that deep-sea trench. Now, in this case, the deep-sea trench probably forms very close to the edge of the continent, maybe not too far off the outer edge of that geocline. But as we continue to do this, just picture your fingers bowing down further and further, and pretty soon the break occurs, and the oceanic lithosphere dives beneath the continental lithosphere. Now remember, that's always the way it is: oceanic lithosphere below continental lithosphere. It's not the other way around. And the reason why is it's a question of density. The density of the continental lithosphere is maybe 2.9, the density of the oceanic lithosphere is about 3.1—light things don't go under heavy things; heavy things go under light things.

So, here we go again. Put your fingers together, and here goes, let's say, your right hand now, diving beneath your left. And if you just picture, now, your left hand—the fingers of your left hand start to curl like that. And, you see, your fingernails are scraping along the back of your hand—which represents, now, this down-going oceanic break, scraping along. Now, in the case of the descending plate, what's doing the scraping is the curled edge, now, of the continental plate. Scraping what? Well, it could be scraping anything off that's on that down-going plate. For example, it'd be scraping off some sediments that were accumulating on the ocean bottom—you're always going to have those. It could actually scrape off a little bit of sedimentary rocks: If they were forming down there, you'd probably have those. Certainly you're going to be scraping off some of the basaltic oceanic crust. And then on top of that, now, we're got some forces here now: We're probably going to do a little bit of *dynamo thermo metamorphism*, so we're going to actually take some of that stuff and metamorphose it a little bit—no great shakes here, but some metamorphic rocks. So we have a mixture, now, of these metamorphic rocks and a little bit of sediments and basaltic rocks. All this now is being thrust upward, okay, as a result, and watch what's going to happen now.

You're going to start filling the deep-sea trench from the bottom up. And as this stuff starts moving toward the surface, this pile of debris can actually build up above the ocean floor and form a ridge all the way along the edge of the continent. Well, we call that an

©2006 The Teaching Company Limited Partnership

accretionary ridge. This stuff—this mixture of things that makes up the accretionary ridge—we use the French word to describe that, and the French word for mixture is *melange*. I just love that word, *melange*. But, anyway, so the melange is the material that makes up the accretionary ridge. Now, if you want to see one, an ancient one, the next time you go to California, take a ride up Highway 1. Highway 1 just rides right up along the coastal range mountains—that is basically an ancient accretionary ridge, and the rocks you see in that area—that would be the melange we're talking about.

Okay, so here we go. We're descending the plate again. We've got the accretionary ridge forming up above the ocean floor now. And now, what's going to happen is sooner or later the plate is going to dive deeply enough that we can start creating molten rock down there. Now, there is a depth that it has to get to apparently. It doesn't start right off the bat. So at certain depths, we're going to start creating *granitic magmas* and *andesitic magmas*. Now, what that depth is, I'm not really sure. But, anyway, once it starts to form now, they start rising toward the surface. The one that gets there first is going to be the andesitic stuff. Remember, that's the stuff that's very low viscosity. So it fights its way up through the outer edge of that geocline and makes it to the surface, which had probably already been uplifted above sea level—so now, much of that geocline is high and dry land. And we start to build, up there on the surface, now, this chain of *continental arc volcanoes*. We're talking *andesitic volcanoes*, and we're talking the *stratovolcanoes*. All the while, of course, here comes, now, this thick, sticky granitic magma coming up into the bottom of that geocline—very, very hot. And all of a sudden, we're talking, now, about metamorphic conditions. We're talking about *contact metamorphism*. We're talking about *dynamo thermal*. We're talking about *hydrothermal*. So a lot of that sediment stuff out at the far edge of that geocline, now, is going to be converted into metamorphic rocks.

So now, note what we've got. We've got this complex mixture of igneous rocks, metamorphic rocks, the melange out there of the accretionary ridge, and on top of it all, you've got this continental arc volcano system. There's your complex core. That's the complex core that parallels the edge of the coast we've been talking about. All the while, what's happening, now, to that stack of sedimentary rocks and what's left of the geocline? Well, now we're talking about compressionary forces—in our case, directed from west to east. So picture, now, this stack of sedimentary rocks just being compressed and folding. We went through all the kinds of folds. I think you understand, now, what's going to happen is the folds are going to change in style as we go from west to east across this geocline. The closest up there to that core in the westernmost edge, you're going to have those highly recumbent—as a matter of fact, we'll probably be down in some of that metamorphose sediments and just the flowage during that dynamo thermal metamorphism that caused this incredible overturning. But as we go further and further east, those are going to turn into the *overturned folds*, and then further, into the *asymmetric folds*. And pretty soon it's going to be into the more *high amplitude symmetrical folds*. And finally, at the far eastern edge of the geocline, now, you're going to have these fairly *low amplitude symmetrical folds*. So you have this, then, fold distribution across the geocline.

Simultaneously with that, we're going to start breaking some rocks now. Just put your hands together—just sort of lace your fingers together and start bending them in the form of a fold now. We're going to make a fold. Note: In between your palms, there are still rocks in there, you see. So here's the deal. If you start unfolding rocks like that—remember now, we're absorbing and consuming energy: plastic deformation—and as we do that, sooner or later the rocks in between your palms are going to get so compacted that the rocks simply aren't able to consume any more. They've consumed about as much as they can, and you're still applying force. They've got to get rid of it, so what they do is they break. And that's why the faults form. Now, the faults we're going to be dealing with— remember, compressional forces—we're going to be dealing with *thrust faults*, *low angle*, and *reverse faults*. And if you look at the faults, the big difference now—again, from west to east throughout the geocline—is the ones in the west are going to be very high displacement (we're going to talk about displacement, perhaps, of tens of miles, who knows how many—maybe a hundred miles in some cases, but very high displacement) and as we go across the geocline heading toward the far eastern edge, what's going to happen is the displacements are just going to get smaller, and smaller, and smaller because you have less and less energy to get rid of, you see. Remember that? And by the time you get all the way over there to that eastern edge, maybe you don't have any faults at all.

So what do we have now? We have a foldbelt mountain range. We've got that complex core along the very edge of the continent, and it consists of that *accretionary wedge*. We're talking about the intrusion of all those granitic magma, and now it's probably exposed by erosion, so you can actually see some of the granitic rocks. We've got the continental arc volcanoes above that. And then landward, we have this whole series of folded and unfolded sedimentary rocks into folded mountain. The picture, that's the Andes: That's exactly how the Andes formed. So if you went to the Andes, that's exactly what you would see.

Okay, let's now take up the next one. The next one is going to be ocean-island arc-continent. Okay, but what we'll eventually get around to, now, is the Japanese Islands. But let's sort of go back before they even formed as we see them today. So the picture, again, is compressive forces. Put your fingers together, and we're going to start making that deep-sea trench. We're going to have the break occur, and, now, this time note: It's oceanic lithosphere diving beneath oceanic lithosphere. Because in this case we're going to have that break occur maybe 100 miles offshore, maybe even more than that. And I've asked a lot of people who supposedly know what they're doing, "Why do you have it form far out like that?" And I've never really gotten a good answer. So, in answer to the question, "Why does it sometimes form so far from the edge of a continent," I really don't know—but, anyway, it does. So, here's the picture, then. We have this accretionary ridge starting to form again—but now it's building from the ocean floor, filling that old deep-sea trench, but now the accretionary ridge is sort of out to sea a little bit further. You see, it's built up above the ocean bottom. Now, the plate is going down once again. Once it gets down deep enough—and it has to get deep enough—now, we have the formation of the granitic magmas and the andesitic magmas. Here come the andesitic magmas to the surface, breaking through to the ocean floor, and they start buildings volcanoes off the ocean floor—but now these are andesitic. These are stratovolcanoes we're talking about. And eventually they build up above sea level, and then we have a chain, now, of these andesitic volcanoes. And what we're talking about, if you want to picture that—that would be the Aleutians.

But we're going to go beyond that now. We're going to keep going, building them higher and higher. But also picture now the granitic magma coming up from below, lifting the whole thing, emplacing itself into this mass of volcanic rocks and freezing and forming these huge masses of granite we call *batholith*. Pretty soon, note what we're doing: We're creating the complex core we talked about before—if you think about the Japanese Islands, that's what they are. If you go to the Japanese Islands, already you have—right offshore—the accretionary ridge. You can go to the Japanese Islands and see places where the rocks have been stripped away, and you can see the granite core of the islands. This is the stuff that was coming up under those volcanoes—and, of course, all the volcanoes you see in the Japanese Islands are andesitic kinds of stratovolcanoes. The classic one, of course, is Mt. Fuji, right outside of Tokyo. So, anyway, the point being you've already formed, today, the complex core we were talking about.

Now, note: Between the Japanese Islands and the mainland of China, Asia, or whatever you want to call it, there's a part of the ocean, and it's called the *Sea of Japan*. We call that a *back arc basin*—*back arc* because, you see, it's behind the arc—the arc would be the volcanic arc of the Japanese Islands. So it's behind that, so we call it a back arc basin. Note the significance of the back arc basin. You've got streams coming down from the mainland, dumping their loads, if you will, into this back arc basin, the Sea of Japan. You've got streams coming off the islands of Japan itself, dumping their loads into the back arc basin. So this is starting to accumulate now, thousands and thousands—and eventually tens of thousands—of feet of sediment that are going to be turned into sedimentary rock—note: That's where we get our sedimentary rocks this time. There is no geocline involved. The only place you have geoclines involved is in opening oceans like the Atlantic. You do not have geoclines involved in closing oceans. But now we've got a sediment stack because it's accumulating in that so-called back arc basin.

Now, here's sort of an interesting sideline. Figure over a period of maybe 50 million years, the land itself could probably be worn down almost to a feature that's playing close to sea level—maybe working, you see, toward its ultimate base level. And all of a sudden, for a while there, the land itself really isn't producing an awful lot of sediment being poured into this basin. But note the significance of that island arc system over there in Japan: It's constantly being renewed. You get rid of one volcano by erosion; you make another one. It's constantly a source of sediment being poured into this back arc basin. So here's the picture as it exists today. Today we see the Japanese Islands. It is the core we talked about—this is the complex core. It's made up of volcanic rocks, metamorphic rocks, igneous rocks, and it's got the accretionary wedge right there.

What's going to happen? Sometime in the future—I don't know how long this is going to take—but what's going to eventually happen is that whole complex of the Japanese Islands is going to start being forced landward. What's going to happen to all those sediments down there in that back arc basin? They're just going to be folded and faulted exactly like we described the geocline in the case of the Andes. The folds are going to change in symmetry across the basin. The displacement of the faults is going to change, but exactly the same thing as you sort-of accordion all those sediments together. Eventually what's going to happen? That whole complex of the Japanese Islands is going to be welded to the edge of the Asian continent: welded—now, we've added to the continent. What happened to all those sediments in that back arc basin? They're going to be thrust up and on top of the continent. So here we have a mountain range, a foldbelt mountain range. We have the complex core along the edge of the continent. We have the folded rocks in the interior. It looks exactly like the Andes. That's what it's going to look like. Note: It formed differently. The only thing different though was how we formed that complex core. We formed it by making that island arc system first. Okay, so much for that one.

Now, on to the big guy: continent-continent collision: These are how the great mountains of the world are created, and so let me set the scene for this one. Let's go back to Pangea. Put Pangea back together again, and we're thinking now strictly of Gondwana, the southern portion. Gondwana was South America on one side of Africa, then bring up Antarctica, and bring over Australia, and bring down India—that basically was Gondwana. And then what happened? Back 200 million years ago, Pangea started breaking up. What happened was that, well, Antarctica slipped down south and located itself at the South Pole. Australia went east and basically opened up what we now know is the Indian Ocean, but I'm interested in that little triangular slab we call India. Here this thing breaks away, and it heads north. Now, remember now, as it heads north it's got its own geocline sitting out in front heading toward Asia. The ocean bottom, then, is being subducted. Where? Just off the coast of Asia.

For example, if we shift to the other side of the ocean, here we have the southern edge of Asia. There is the zone of subduction that's eating up the ocean bottom as India comes closer and closer. We have an accretionary ridge. And this time, the accretionary ridge apparently built very, very high above the ocean—so in itself it's probably a pretty good size mountain range unto itself. And then we have the complex behind, which would be the intruded igneous rocks and that continental volcanics, just like the Andes. They're sitting there, all the volcanic activity. Note: Between the complex back there, where the volcanoes are, and the accretionary ridge, there's a basin in there—and we call that a *fore-arc basin*. Fore-arc because it's in front of the volcanic arc, you see, as opposed to back arc basin. Well, this fore-arc basin is pretty good-sized too. I mean, it's accumulating sediment, and over the time it's going to have, you know, tens of thousands of feet of sediments in there, turned into tens of thousands of feet of sedimentary rock. So now, the scene is set. Here comes India—closer, and closer, and closer. And pretty soon the front edge, now, of India's geocline is going run into the accretionary ridge of Asia. Now, picture what's going to happen. When those two collide, what's going to happen to India's geocline? It's going to be thrust to the south, up and on top of the Indian plane. It's going to be folded and faulted exactly the way we discussed before—so there's a foldbelt mountain range right there.

But what happened to the fore-arc basin? It had probably as much as sediment in it as the geocline. It was thrust northward up on top of Asia. So, note the difference: We've got two, now, foldbelt mountain ranges, in between which we have all this crystalline core. So, it's a little bit different scenario. But here's an important thing. Picture, now, the oceanic lithosphere being subducted underneath the edge of Asia. Right behind it, of course, you have this continental lithosphere: India is coming along. And all of a sudden, the last bit, now, of the oceanic lithosphere dives down and is sucked down into that zone of subduction. Right behind it it's pulling, now, the continental lithosphere. The continental lithospheres don't like to go under there, you see. They don't like to subduct. So, it's fighting it all the way, but it's being pulled down under.

Well, what's going to happen? Remember, that's low-density rock, and as a result it's going to try to rise and does. And as a result, that entire mass is going to be uplifted, and that's the reason why the Himalaya are as high as they are. The reason why the Himalaya are as high as they are—and they are still rising as a matter of fact—is due to the buoyancy, now, of that portion of the Indian continental lithosphere that was dragged down underneath that subduction zone. So, anyway, there's your Himalaya. But note the big difference: We've got two foldbelt mountains centered with a complex core. Well, that's forming now. When did that happen? Well, it all started about 45 million years ago. I think if you think back—remember, we were talking about the change in direction of the Emperor Seamounts, when we were talking about the Hawaiian Islands—that bend. That was 45 million years of that supposedly happening. So, anyway, I said that it may have formed as a result of the collision of India with Asia. Just picture what this collision was like. There was enough energy dissipated: It could indeed have changed the movement of all the plates.

I want to show you another example, now, of another continent-continent collision, and I want to do this because this comes a little closer to home. So let's go back and set the scene again. Let's go back in time to about, let's say, 350 million years. Back 350 million years ago, Pangea was in the process of being created, and it was almost finished. But we've got one big collision to go before we create Pangea. So here's the picture I want you to have: Over to the west, we want to have a very, very large continent, and we call it *Laurentia*. Laurentia would be sort of the mixture, today, of all of what is North America plus Greenland. That would have been Laurentia. Over to the east now, we have another very large continental mass, and that one is what we call *Gondwana*—and mostly, in this case, it would be the African part, the North African part of Gondwana. In between now, we have an ocean called the *Iapetus Ocean*. So, what's going to happen, now, is these two are coming together, so we're trying to finish off the formation of Pangea. Let's see, about 300 million years ago those two collided—and as a result, it was a continent-continent collision. As a result, there was a mountain range formed that had this crystalline core—this mixture of igneous rocks, and metamorphic rocks, and volcanic rocks. And on both sides now—to the west and to the east—we have these folded mountains of sedimentary rocks. So it looked exactly like, basically, the Himalaya looked today.

Well, Pangea wasn't together very long, and about 150 million years later it started breaking up. And so, here, 200 million years ago,

Pangea breaks up, and the break, now, we're talking about occurred apparently right down the middle, now, of that very complex core. So what happened when it broke up is we had one continent going to the west—that was going to become North America—and it's taking with it half of that complex core and one of those folded mountain ranges, you see. The other one heads east—that's North Africa, of course. And it takes with it the other half of the crystalline core and its folded mountain range, and it's heading east. And what we're creating, of course, is the Atlantic Ocean. Now, over a period of probably by 100 million years later, let's talk about North America.

By 100 million years later, those grand mountains that have been created—and there's no reason to believe when that collision occurred it didn't create a range of mountains every bit as grand as the Himalaya—well, by 100 million years later, any surface expression that was ever there in the area of North America probably eroded away. We're probably having eroded very close to sea level, and so it would have sort of been a very sort-of flat, featureless place—we sort-of picture it. Note: The structures are still below—the structures are still down there. So then what happened? Well, what happened was starting about 60 million years ago the entire eastern margin of North America was uplifted in a broad, broad arch. Now, it really isn't a domal thing. It's simply a compressional thing, apparently, that simply arched everything from about what is now the Mississippi River all the way—actually beyond our present shoreline, probably out to the outer edge of what is now the continental shelf. The elevation to which it was uplifted? Not very much—about 6,000 feet.

But here's the deal: As it was uplifted even 6,000 feet, streams started to be rejuvenated again—they started to wear down through again, carving away. And the streams, as they sculpted the new landscape, were influenced by the structures below—by the rock types they ran into. If they ran into, for example, relatively soft rocks, they cut deeper than if they ran into relatively hard rocks. So we started to evolve a brand new topography. Now, the topography that was created over the last 60 million years, that's what the Appalachians are. Note the topography you see: If you drive through the Appalachians the topography you see basically was formed during the last 60 million years as a result of this domal uplift. But the structures that you see—as you drive through the Appalachians and you see rocks on end and broken and bent—that was all created

©2006 The Teaching Company Limited Partnership

back 300 million years ago when these two finally collided together to make that grand mountain range.

Now, where are the pieces now? Well, if we think about that crystalline core, that complex core—we can see it today. Well, some places we can see it. That's basically the Piedmont: Remember, I said the outer-most portion, the eastern portion, of the Appalachians is called the Piedmont. The Piedmont: highly metamorphosed rocks, highly recumbent folding, all kinds of volcanic intrusions, and all kinds of mixtures—that was that really crystalline core that we're talking about. As you come in and get to the Blue Ridge—the Blue Ridge has some of that, but it's probably, maybe, the edge of that highly deformation part. But going from the Great Valley now, starting with the Great Valley and going all the way westward to the edge of what is now Appalachia—which would be somewhere around the edge of West Virginia, eastern Ohio—that would have been that stack of sedimentary rocks that had been folded and faulted into folds that progressively changed. Remember, we went through that—highly overturned next to the Blue Ridge, and then dying out to those low amplitude folds in the far western portion. That's basically what that is: That's the folded part.

Here's a question for you: Where's the other half? Where's the other half now? If you wanted to see the other half—the mirror image, if you will—of the Appalachians, where would you go? Well, you'd go to Africa, because, remember, it went with Africa when Africa took off in the other direction. Over in Africa there's a mountain range, and it's called the *Atlas Mountains*. They're called the Atlas Mountains, and they look exactly like, structurally, exactly like the Appalachians—except they're just simply a mirror image. So, there's one of the evidences that they finally saw to really prove that those two continents were together. Okay, so there's the Appalachians, and they don't look like much today, perhaps, to a lot of people—but these were once one of the grandest mountains in the world.

Just to sort of close this thing off: How about the future? What's going to be next? Well, of course, this is easy to predict because no one will know for sure if I'm right or not. But, anyway, as I look at a map, and I look at continents, and I look at where all the zones of subduction are—I look, for example, at Africa and Europe. There's a zone of subduction down through the Mediterranean Sea. That tells me, you see, that somebody is closing up there. The ocean bottom—

which is now the Mediterranean—is being consumed by that zone of subduction. That tells me that some time in the future, Africa may run into Europe. And as grand as the Alps are today, they're going to be added to—and so, perhaps, in the future, you're going to have a mountain range there that's equal in grandeur to the present-day Himalaya.

The other one I sort of look at, too, is Australia. You have Australia, and then—far to the north, of course—you've got the mainland of China, but in between there you've got a zone of subduction. This is that Indonesian zone of subduction where you hear all the volcanic eruptions lately, and the earthquakes lately. Well, that tells me that the ocean bottom is being consumed. That tells me that Australia is moving northward. Now, note: One of the things that tells me is that that eastern-most portion of the Indian Ocean seems to be now going closed, remember Wilson's Cycle? Sooner or later in 50 million years everybody is going to start closing up. I think that's probably evidence that maybe the eastern portion is already starting to close.

How long will any kind of a collision take to occur between Australia and the mainland of China? Well, it's going to be a very, very long time, even geologically. But all the evidence says it seems to be that it's going in that direction. So if I had to predict where the next mountain building was going to go on after the one we're experiencing now with the Himalaya, I would say it would be Africa against Europe. And the one after that, a long time in the future, I would say Australia, perhaps, with the mainland of China. But the point is—and I hope you get this feeling—that the Earth is a very, very dynamic thing. It isn't just sitting there. It's always moving and changing. What the Earth looks like today is not what it looked like yesterday, and it's not going to be looking like that tomorrow. It's always, always, always changing, as opposed to the old idea— remember, when we first started talking to each other, we said the old idea was where the continents are and the oceans are today, that's where they've always been. No. No, the Earth is constantly changing all the time, in big ways—mountain building; in little ways—slumps and erosion, but it's changing all the time.

Lecture Thirty-Five
Economic Geology of Coal

Scope:

Coal comes from wood that has been preserved in environments where oxygen and microbial activity is low. Its use as an energy source dates from the invention of the steam engine in the early 1700s. Coal can be ranked in terms of its carbon content, which is also the source of its energy, measured in British Thermal Units (BTUs). Coal's quality can be measured according to its sulfur and aluminum content. Appalachian coal and coal from the western United States are high in quality, though the western coal is low in rank. In order to comply with a law requiring a sulfur content of less than 12%, coal can be cleaned through various processes, including *scrubbers* and *getters*.

Outline

I.   Economic geology is the use of materials for the benefit of society. Coal and petroleum comprise 90% of all the energy budgeted in the United States.

   A. Coal comes from preserved wood. Good preservers of wood are swamps, where the oxygen content and microbial activity are very low. Microbial activity is lowered at pH levels of less than 3.

   B. Peat is wood that has been preserved in a swamp. When peat is buried, it becomes coal.

   C. Coal became a major source of energy when Thomas Newcomen invented the steam engine in 1705. It was James Watts who made the engine work. The first fuel was wood, which proved impractical. Thus, coal became the primary fuel and remained so until the early 1900s, when petroleum took over.

II. Two important aspects of coal are *rank* and *quality*.

   A. Rank is about carbon. Any organic material comprises carbon and volatiles. The carbon content of coal can be ranked.

      1. Wood has about 45% carbon.

    2. Peat has about 55% carbon.

    3. *Lignite* (also called *brown coal*) has about 65% carbon.

    4. Subbituminous coal has about 75% carbon.

    5. Bituminous coal has more than 85% carbon.

    6. Anthracite has more than 95% carbon.

B. Energy is stored in carbon and can be measured in BTUs (British thermal units) per pound of dry weight. Wood has 4,500 BTUs per pound, while anthracite has 15,000 BTUs per pound.

C. In the eastern United States, the coal is primarily bituminous. In the western United States, the coal is mostly lignite or subbituminous. Anthracite is relatively scarce anywhere in the world.

D. Coal quality is measured in terms of ash and sulfur.

    1. The source of sulfur, one of the six elements required for life (along with carbon, oxygen, hydrogen, nitrogen, and phosphorous), is the tree itself.

    2. Ash is silicon and aluminum that the tree rejects and stores in dead wood cells. (Note that the only living wood in a tree is the layer right below the bark. The rest of the interior of the tree is dead wood.) High-quality coal has less than 10% ash and less than 1% sulfur. Medium-quality coal has 30% ash and 3% sulfur.

    3. High-quality coal comes from the southern Appalachian Basin and medium-quality from the northern Appalachian Basin. All coals in the western United States are high quality, though lower in rank.

III. Today, so-called *steam coal* is used to generate steam to drive turbine engines and make electricity.

A. Coal would be a great fuel if it were not for the sulfur in it. Until 1970, any kind of coal could be burned, but of course, its sulfur content reacting with water in the atmosphere resulted in acid rain.

B. In 1970, the Environmental Protection Agency clean air laws were enacted, which prescribed a *compliance coal* that has less than 1.2% sulfur. All western coals are compliance coals. Most of the coals from the eastern United States are non-compliance coals.

C. The production of compliance coals from non-compliance coals can be accomplished in two ways: (1) *cleaning* and (2) *blending*.

1. **Cleaning:** In coals where the total sulfur is in excess of 1%, most of the additional sulfur is in the form of pyrite. Because pyrite is denser than the coal itself, total sulfur can be reduced by crushing the coal into a fine powder and subjecting it to float/sink separation, which removes that fraction of the coal rendered denser by the presence of pyrite and leaves the remaining coal lower in total sulfur.

2. **Blending:** Blending involves mixing high quality compliance coal with non-compliance coal to produce a mix with less than 1.2% sulfur.

D. Two devices can be introduced into power-plant design to minimize the amount of SO_x gases vented to the atmosphere: (1) *scrubbers* and (2) *getters*.

1. **Scrubbers:** A scrubber is literally a washing machine that "scrubs" the gases emerging from the firebox with an alkaline solution that precipitates the SO_x gases as an inert sulfate.

2. **Getters:** Another cleaning device is a *getter*. The coal is powdered, and with limestone powder, it is blasted into the firebox. As the coal burns, the sulfur generates SO_x gases. The limestone decomposes into carbon dioxide and calcium oxide; these elements "get" the SO_x gases, creating calcium sulphate, which is benign. The sulfur content of the fuel is monitored, and a computer calculates how much calcium oxide is needed. Note that the fuel can be any material with an organic content greater than 25%, including low-quality coals or *gob*, a product of coal cleaning.

E. Much has been learned about acid rain. Active mines know how to control and neutralize acid production. Much of the acid production today comes from old, abandoned, deep mines.

F. Coal could provide a much-needed energy source for the future.

Recommended Reading:

Thomas, L., *Coal Geology*.

Questions to Consider:

1. How do the eastern and western coals of the United States compare in rank and quality?

2. What is the source of the ash and sulfur found in coal?

Lecture Thirty-Five—Transcript
Economic Geology of Coal

I've decided to devote the last two lectures of the course to a study of economic geology, the use of natural materials for the benefit of society. And the two materials I've chosen to talk about are coal and petroleum. And I chose those because those two materials provide 90% of all the energy budget of this country, and I've always been convinced that most people don't really know enough about where we are and where we're going. So that's my purpose in these two discussions we're going to have at the end, is to give you some idea what coal and petroleum is all about, where we are now, what the future that lies ahead looks like.

First of all, coal. Actually this is sort of my specialty area so I sort of have a soft heart for coal here. I'm a coal geochemist by trade, I guess. Anyway, the source of coal—where does it come from? It comes from land plants: in particular it comes from the wood of land plants. As a matter of fact, if you hold a lump of coal in your hand, basically what you're holding in your hand is preserved wood. So that's where it comes from. Just think about, now, when the average falls out in the woods without any time passing at all it's gone. It's decomposed. It's eaten up by microbial activity. So if you're going to preserve it to make it into anything, you have to keep away from oxygen and microbial activity. And the environment that does that is a swamp. Now, we spend a lot of time in swamps trying to figure out how these worked. And it's very simple it turns out. The reason why they're so good at preserving the woody tissues—or any organic matter for that matter—is: number one, the oxygen content is very low. In swamps the oxygen content of the water is very low for two reasons. Number one, the water moves very, very, very slowly so it's not being aerated like a bubbling stream, you see. And the other thing is that there's all kinds of carbon material around: it sucks up oxygen and makes carbon dioxide. So the idea is the oxygen is very low, you don't have to worry about oxidizing these materials.

Now, the other thing you have to do, though, is sort of keep the microbial activity down. And these microbial activities are directed primarily by the pH of the water, of the solution. And microbes really do their best job at about pH 7. So what we found was that if you have a swamp and you want to preserve enough of the material, ultimately to make good coal, the pH of the swamp had to be at least less than 3 and preferably less than 2. In a lot of the measurements we took in swamps like that, it was down around 1½ and things like that. So anyway, we had the conditions then to allow the stuff to be preserved. Right within the swamp it turns into a material called peat, and you've heard of peat of course. And the only difference, actually, between the peat that you're familiar with that you put in your garden and the peat I'm talking about is that the stuff you put in your garden is made from sphagnum moss, which really doesn't have much wood in it. And the stuff I'm talking about is loaded with woody tissue. So that's the only real difference between them.

Then what we're going to do is we're going take the peat to bury it—not very deep—you don't want a lot of pressure on it; not very hot—you don't want to heat it up too far, maybe a few hundred degrees centigrade. And it goes through a sort of a baking process where it changes from peat into the various forms of coal. And, you know, a lot of people, including myself, have tried to reproduce that process, and I, personally, have never been able to do it. I've never been able to take woody tissue or peat tissues of any kind and turn them into anything that even faintly resembled coal. So the actual process is still sort of a mystery to me, actually how that's done.

Anyway, a little bit of history. I don't know how long people have been burning coal. I'm sure it goes back a thousand years. Somebody had to find this lump of black stuff and when they threw it on the fire, it burned and kept them warm. So I don't know really how long that's been going on. But coal as a major energy source really had to wait until the invention of the steam engine. The steam engine was invented in the early 1700s by an inventor by the name of Thomas Newcomen. And he invented this engine, but it didn't run very well. And it took another inventor by the name of James Watt to really get it working. So James Watt is oftentimes given the credit for inventing it. He really didn't invent the steam engine, but he certainly made the one work. The first fuel that was used was wood. And very soon, they realized that wood was not going to make it because wood doesn't have enough heat potential to provide the steam they needed to drive the engines. And thank God for that, because if they would have cut down every tree in Europe. If you ever go to Scotland—where my people are from—if you ever go to the Highlands of Scotland, they're barren. They weren't then, they were covered with trees, and they were all chopped down to provide fuel for these new steam engines. And only now, is a matter of fact, are they starting to replant a lot of those slopes.

Anyway, they looked around for another resource, and one thing Scotland has is coal. So coal came on to the scene. Coal was the energy source for the newfangled steam engine. It's what drove the industrial revolution, which is always dated somewhere in the mid-1700s. It drove the locomotive across the country. It drove the steamships. And coal remained the number one energy source, actually until the early 1900s, when petroleum took over largely because of the introduction of the gasoline-powered automobile. So anyway, there's a little history for you.

First thing. To understand coal there really are only two things you really have to know: you have to know what rank is and you have to know about coal quality. These are totally different. A lot of people think they're the same or related somehow, but they're not related in any way. *Rank*, what it's all about is carbon. *Quality's* about ash and sulfur. Let's take up the rank first. Carbon, if you take any organic stuff—I don't really care what it is—as a chemist I will look upon any organic material as being made of two fundamentally different components: carbon and everything else. The everything else we sort of lump together and call *volatiles*. The reason why is because they can be driven off by heating. So carbon is the important part here.

And so what's the important part of carbon? Well, we want to make a little sort of chart here to list the various forms of coal and indicate how much carbon we're dealing with. Let's start off with wood. This is the source of all the coal, so if we look at wood the concentration of carbon in wood is about maybe 45% carbon, 55% volatiles. As a matter of fact, you've seen the results of that: you burn a log in the fireplace, all the flames. Any time you see flames, that's the volatiles burning. And sooner or later the flames die down and then the carbon starts to burn. That's where you really get your heat. So anyway, 45% of wood is carbon.

But then what we're going to do is make it into peat. Right in the swamp, now, what's going to start to happen is simply going to drive off these volatiles. If you ever go into a swamp—which I doubt you will—one of the things you'll see are bubbles coming to the surface all the time. A lot of that is simply the volatiles being driven off from the peaty material as its being created. So if you go to peat now, it has roughly 55% of carbon, so we're increasing it a little bit. And then the rest of it, taking the peat and burying it, just a slow cooker kind of thing. All we're going to do now, is simply keep driving off volatiles and increasing the carbon content. So if you increase the carbon content to maybe 65% now, you've got what we call *lignite*. Well, around the world lignite is called *brown coal* because it's blocky—it looks like coal, but it's not black: it's brown in color. Then if we keep driving off some more volatiles and we get up to maybe 75% carbon, now we've got *subbituminous coal*. And if we keep going and we get up to 85%, then we've got *bituminous coal*. And if we can drive up to greater than 95% carbon, then we have *anthracite*. Well, that column right there, from peat at the bottom to anthracite at the top that's the *rank series*. Those of us who study coal consider peat the lowest rank of coal and, of course, anthracite is the highest rank so note the only difference in the coal is simply the carbon content. So that's what determines rank.

Well, so what? The so what is the energy. Picture a tree growing out there in the sunlight and it's doing its photosynthesis thing and all that kind of stuff. But it knows it has to suffer over the night. The sun goes down, it's not going to generate any energy, and so it has to store a little bit of energy so where does it store it? It stores in the carbon. And around here for example, the temperate climates, they lose their leaves for half of the year, there's no photosynthesis going on but they need to store energy to get it over to the spring until the leaves come back. Where do they store it? They store it in the carbon. You want to get it back, you simply take carbon, you burn it, carbon dioxide, and the heat comes out. So, for example, when you're burning that log in your fireplace, think about this: the heat that's coming out from that log basically what it is is solar energy that was stored in the wood of the tree during whatever time the tree was alive before you chopped it down and burned it. So anyway, that's the importance of carbon.

What if we go back to our little chart now, and look at carbon content and heat content now. The measure of heat content is BTUs per pound, British Thermal Use per pound dry weight. If we look at wood for example, wood has about maybe 4,500 BTUs per pound dry weight. That sounds like a big number but actually it's pretty low. As matter of fact, that was so low, that's the reason why they had to give up using wood for fuel—because it simply didn't have the BTU potential that they needed. Now, if you go up this list—

now, I always tell students, I don't like to give them numbers to memorize so I'm just going to give you the number at the top of the list to give you a feeling for how it changes. At the top of the list you, get up to the anthracite, we're talking 15,000 BTUs per pound. So anyway, there's a big difference as you go up the chart because BTU content increases all the time as rank increases. What does it mean? It means if you're in the business of buying coal, to burn to make heat, to make steam, to drive a turbine, to make electricity, what you're going to want to do, you're going to want to buy the highest rank of coal you can.

Well, what if we look at a map of the old United States to see where the coal is. In the United States the map shows we have two basic areas of coal production, eastern United States and western. If you look at the eastern United States, basically we've got a very few, fairly large basins. You have, for example, what we call the Mid-Continent Basin, that's the biggest one of all. Then you have an Illinois Basin. There's actually a Michigan Basin, but we don't produce any coal from the Michigan Basin. Then you have the Appalachian Basin, a fairly big basin. And if you look at all of those, basically what those all are, that's all bituminous coal. Well, except over in the easternmost part of Pennsylvania, Scranton and Wilkes-Barre they have a little a bit of anthracite but the point about anthracite is that there really isn't much anthracite anywhere in the world. It's sort of a rare bird. So basically, then, your eastern coals are largely bituminous coal.

If we go out west the thing you'll notice from the map is that you have a lot of small basins. And of all of those there is one that does produce bituminous coal. That would be the Book Cliffs area of Utah, and that is bituminous. But all of the others, basically, are lower rank: they're either lignite or sub-bituminous. So note: pound for pound eastern coals are better than western coals in terms of generating power. So anyway, if you're out to buy coal, it looks to me like you probably want to buy eastern coals rather than western.

Well, there's something else we have to consider. We have to consider now, coal quality. *Coal quality* is determined by two things ash and sulfur. Now, the first point is: these go hand in hand. In other words, when one goes up the other goes up, when one goes down the other goes down. The reason why is they both come from the stuff, they both come from the plant, they both come from the wood. Now, why do they go hand in hand? Sulfur coming from the wood? Yeah, if you think about all living things—life as we know it—there are six elements that are required: carbon, oxygen, hydrogen, nitrogen, phosphorous, and sulfur. So the sulfur comes right from the plant itself, so there's the source of the sulfur. How about the ash? Well, this is sort of an interesting one. Picture that tree growing out there again. It takes water out of the ground, passes the water up through the tree, takes out whatever nutrients it wants, and eventually the water gets to the leaves has and is transpired out into the atmosphere.

But there are certain elements that trees just don't want. As a matter of fact, there are certain elements that plants in general don't want, and the two in particular are aluminum and silicone. They just don't want those things. But here's the problem: unless they get rid of them somehow, if it gets to the end of the trail, and they're up there in that leaf and the water's transpired, all that stuff deposits in the leaves. And as a result the leaves are going to be blocked up, and as a result that plant's going to die. So they have to do something with this. What do they do with it? Well, what they do with it is they stash it away in the old dead wood cells. I think most of you know that when you talk about wood, the only living wood is that layer right below the bark, the so-called *cambium layer*. That's this year's ring. All the other ones on the inside are all dead, and they're all empty. So what the plants do, they just stash all the stuff they really don't want into those dead wood cells. And so the thing is when you burn, for example, a log in your fire place, that's what you see in the way of ash. That's simply the stuff that the tree stored in the wood that it didn't want. Well, if you take that wood and turn it into coal the ash just goes right along with that. In other words, there's the ash. The ash simply represent the materials that the tree really didn't want.

Now, in terms of quality, we usually break down quality into high, medium, and low quality. A high quality coal would be any coal that has less than 10% ash, 1% sulfur; less than 10% ash, 1% sulfur. I would consider that a high quality coal. Now, the dividing line between medium and low isn't really so agreed upon as we agree on that one because it really depends upon what you're using the coal for and how you're using it. But I would say that the dividing line between medium and low would be maybe 30% ash, 3% sulfur. If you get more than 30% ash and 3% sulfur you've got pretty poor coal.

Well, so the quality is an important thing now. Let's go back to our map. We go back to our map and we look at, say, the eastern coals.

Question: do we have high quality coals in the East? Yeah, we do, sure we do. For example, if you took the Appalachian Basin and you drew a line east-west through the Appalachian Basin, right about through the middle of West Virginia, that line you drew that is 10% ash, 1% sulfur. Below that, the southern Appalachian Basin—all those coals are indeed high quality. They're all less than 10% ash, 1% sulfur. But once you go to the north, for example, the northern Appalachian Basin, now, we're talking medium quality. Now, they're greater than 10% ash, 1% sulfur. Case in point: the Pittsburgh coal, one bed of coal alone, represents 25% of the total production in West Virginia. Now, West Virginia, Kentucky, and Wyoming are always vying for number one, every month, to see who produces the most. But 25% of the West Virginia's production is that one coal bed in Pittsburgh: ash content about 15%, sulfur content about 2.1%. So note it's not a high quality coal. If you go out to the Illinois Basin, they only mine one coal out there it's called a Herrin Number 6. They have one medium quality coal, and then the rest are pretty poor. That great big field, that big Mid-Continent, most of those are very poor to medium at very, very best. So anyway, the problem with the eastern coals, you see, they're high in rank, so we gain there, but they're lower in quality. On the other hand, if we go out west, all those coals out West, regardless they're all high quality all of them are less than 10% ash, 1% sulfur. So there's the big difference then between the two areas of coal. The eastern coals are higher in rank but basically lower in quality. The western coals, although they're lower in rank, are all high in quality.

Now, the question is, now, what are you going to use this stuff for? Well, today we might as well just talk about today. As we speak, every ton of coal that's mined in the United States goes to make one thing: and that's to generate steam, to drive turbines, to make electricity. So we call that *steam coal*. Well, here's the point: up until 1970 you could burn any coal you wanted. There was no law that restricted what the quality of the coal, what the rank of the coal, what anything. You could burn anything you want to make steam to produce electricity. Up until that time. The problem, then, was that coal would be a great, great fuel if it wasn't for sulfur. Because here's the deal. When you burn the coal in the firebox, the sulfur burns too. It burns, oxidizes, and turns into SO_2, SO_3, we just call SO_X: the X simply refers to two or three. So you produce these SO_Xes. If the SO_Xes then are allowed to get into the atmosphere and react with water in the atmosphere, they produce sulfurous and sulfuric acids. These are very nasty acids. That was the basis for the old acid rain problems. And up until the 70s it was a very, very, very bad problem. If acid rain gets into a lake, it'll sterilize it just like right now. Leaching through soil—it takes the nutrients out of soil. Trees succumb to it. Conifers for example, are especially prone to being killed off by acid rain. It was a very, very bad thing.

Well, what happened in 1970 is the EPA Clean Air laws kicked into effect and part of that said you can't do that anymore. You cannot burn all that high sulfur coal anymore. They describe what they call a compliance coal. Now, what a *compliance coal* is: basically it's a coal that has less 1.2% sulfur. Well, note: right off that bat, all of the Western coals are compliance coals. They don't have to worry about it out there: they're all compliance coals. In the Appalachian Basin we do have, in the southern coal fields, we do have compliance coals. But note: everywhere else in the East, they're noncompliant. Pittsburgh coal 2.1%—that's a noncompliance coal. Question: what do you do with this stuff? What do you with this stuff? Well, you somehow have to clean it up. Well, the way we clean it up: there are a couple things we can do it. One of the things we can do is we actually clean the coal. We call it *coal cleaning,* and here's what we do: we crush the coal up into a relatively fine powder. The problem is now, if the sulfur goes over 1%, the reason why it goes over 1% is the formation of this mineral you've all heard of fool's gold, pyrite, iron disulfide, that's what makes the sulfur go high. Well, if you somehow can get rid of the pyrite out of the coal, then you can reduce the sulfur content. So what we do is we have these cleaning plants, so-called, and what the do is they crush the coal up and put it through a float/sink system. And what happens the pyrite containing coals fall to the bottom, and they take the ones that don't have pyrite off the top and so we've cleaned the coal.

Question: can you take a "dirty coal," if you will, and clean it up and make it a compliance coal? Yeah, sometimes you can. Sometimes you can't. Well, let's say you can't. What else can you do? Well, one of the other things we can do is we can blend. What blending means is very simple. You get out of southern West Virginia, for example, and you buy some of that really high quality coal, and then you blend it with the not high quality coal, as long as you can get the overall concentration of sulfur down below 1.2%. So, if you look at the eastern part of the United States, there are not very many power plants east of the Mississippi that don't blend coals from a number of different sources just to get their compliance coal. So we can do that, and we do do that.

What else could we do? Well, there's two other things that we could do. Starting in 1985, by law all the new power plants had to have what we call a scrubber on board. A scrubber. And as a matter of fact, all the old ones have to start installing scrubbers to perform this task. Here's what a *scrubber* is. It's very simple actually, it's a washing machine is what it is. For example, consider the firebox and you're burning the coal and you're making those S-O-X gasses, those SO_X gasses. You don't want them to go up the stack because they're going to produce that sulfurous and sulfuric acid up there. So here's what you do: between the firebox and the stack you install this thing called a scrubber. What happens is the SO_X gasses come out of a firebox into a scrubber and you scrub it. With what? Water. In other words what you're going to do—note— is you're taking that reaction that's reacts sulfur oxides with water to make the acids into the scrubber. Now you've got the acid generated. All you have to do now is neutralize it. How do you do that? Well, this water we're talking about really isn't pure water. It's probably a solution of either calcium hydroxide or sodium hydroxide, most of which you remember are very strong bases. So it reacts with acids as they're created in the scrubber and what do you end up with? You end up with calcium sulfate or sodium sulfate. Well, calcium sulfate, for example, that's anhydrite, it's a benign thing. You can take those things out of the scrubber, and you can put them in your backyard. They're not going to hurt anything because they don't produce any acid; they're simply benign.

So note what we do with the scrubbers. What the scrubbers do is basically they take those acids and rather than allowing to form in the atmosphere and make acid rain, they're forming them right in the scrubber. And as a result, the stuff that goes up the stack basically is not polluting the atmosphere at all. Again, all power plants since 1985 are required by law to have them. All the old ones are being forced to install them. A lot of the companies are sort of resisting because it's very expensive, but they will otherwise they'll be forced out of business. Okay, so that's the scrubber, and it's very, very, very effective. The scrubbers really do a very, very good job.

Now, what about this other one, there's a thing called a *getter*. Maybe I'll just describe how it works then you're see how this thing really gets the name the getter. What the getter is, it's limestone. What they do with the limestone is they grind it into a powder just like a talcum powder. Then they mix it with the coal. Now, here's a point I forgot to mention. Whenever this coal goes into these power plants, I mean, they're not shoveling it in there in chunks, what they do with the coal is they powder it. The coal almost has the consistency of talcum powder, too. So what they do is they blend the limestone powder with the coal powder, and they blast this thing into the firebox. Now, as the coal is burning, picture what happens, now, to the sulfur. The sulfur is generating those SO_X gasses in the firebox. But what happens to the limestone? The limestone decomposes into calcium oxide and carbon dioxide. The carbon dioxide goes up the stack, but the calcium oxide then looks around and sees those SO_X gasses and goes and gets them, you see—and that's why they call them getters—and it creates calcium sulfate. Once again we're talking anhydrite here. That stuff is then taken out with the ash. And again it's totally benign. So note with the getter the SO_X gasses don't even get out of the firebox.

Now, these systems are very, very sophisticated. For example, we have a plant like that in Morgantown, and what they do is monitor the sulfur content of the fuel. Now, I say fuel because it doesn't necessarily have to be coal. They can burn anything that has an organic content greater than 25%. All right, so for example, in Morgantown they're burning a mixture of 40% coal, of any sulfur content, and 60% gob. Now, *gob*, what we mean by gob. You know that stuff that was taking out of those cleaning plants that concentrated all that pyrite in there? A very high sulfur content. That's what they're burning. The reason why we're burning it is because there's still a lot an awful lot of organic material with that coal. It's still coal, you see, but the fact that it has all that pyrite in it is what used to make it non-usable. Now, we don't have to worry. So we mix it together and here's the way it works. They constantly monitor the composition of the fuel. They constantly monitor the sulfur content, and then the computer calculates exactly how much calcium carbonate should be added to the mix in order to take care of the all SO_X gasses that will be produced. And as a result it doesn't make any difference what you're burning anymore. So note, for example, we talked about medium quality coals, and poor quality coals, or low quality—you can burn any coal now. You can burn anything at all in these plants, and that's the advantage of the getters. These are very, very, very, very efficient.

The idea is between the so-called scrubbers and the so-called getters, I think the day of the air polluting, coal burning, power plant is just about to the end. Whenever we get the old plants brought around—and we're starting to take care of them by either installing scrubbers or by installing the technology of the getters—I think the idea of acid rain will be a thing of the past.

Now, there are still some problems we have. For example, we still have this problem in the East of acid mine drainage. Whenever you mine coal the coal of the associated rocks has this pyrite in it. Whenever pyrite oxidizes and is put in the solution, it generates sulfuric acid. This stuff gets in the water and pollutes it, but here's the deal. People like me, that's been my research for probably for a couple of decades, and a lot of us have been working on this problem of acid mine drainage. And we have learned an awful lot about how it's created. And not only that, how you can slow it down or even stop the creation of it. And the companies have listened to us. So if you come in to the eastern part of the United States today and you look at active mines, the mining operators today are pretty good. They can go in, and they can mine coal in either the surface or the subsurface—underground mining—and they know how to control the acid production. They know how to neutralize the acid production. So if you come into the modern type of mining operation in the East today, you'll find out that acid mine drainage is not a problem anymore. They know how to reclaim the land and put it back to active use without being its decimated by all this acid production. The acid source today in the East—in all of the Appalachian area and all the entire East—doesn't come from active mines: it comes from old abandoned deep mines. I'm talking about mines that were in operation in the early part of the 1900s that have abandoned for 50 years. The problem with a lot of these is, we can't even find out where they where. We have no mine maps. If we can find out where the mines are, then we can go in and try to attack the acid production at the source. Right now, what we have to do is simply take the acid as it comes out of the ground and sit there and treat it forever. Well, that's going to be a real problem. But I think that's going to be solved too.

Here's the bottom line: whenever you start thinking about energy, and you start thinking about coal, the question arises, "Yeah, but how much of this stuff do we have?" I always say that coal is to the United States what oil is to Saudi Arabia. We have more coal than anybody in the world. We have enough coal in this country to provide 100%, now, 100% is estimated we could provide all the energy we needed in this country from coal alone, and we could do that for about 250 years. So you see, when it comes to an energy problem, we really have to start looking at coal again. It's number two energy source today. There's a bad feeling in a lot of people's minds about coal and the mining of coal, and I understand that. But I think we have to realize in the future we're going to need energy, and I hope to convince you in the next lecture, we talk about just how badly we're going to be in need of it and how soon we're going to be in need of it. And as a coal geologist, of course, I would suggest we have to start looking back at coal again. I predict—and you heard it here first—I predict that coal will rise again in importance. It may not rise to number one, but I think we're going to see the amount of energy generated in this country from coal is going to be greater than 28% in the not too distant future. The next one we want to talk about is petroleum, and that's the topic of the next lecture.

Lecture Thirty-Six
Economic Geology of Petroleum

Scope:

Petroleum is formed when marine material is preserved and buried in highly porous and permeable reservoirs that are capped by rock that prevents the petroleum oil and gas from escaping. The United States is highly dependent on the production of oil. Predictions about the inevitable diminution and elimination of oil resources appear to be all too accurate. For this reason, various proposals for increasing the self-sufficiency of the United States in energy sources have emerged. These proposals include the manufacture of ethanol and liquefied natural gas, which can be used for transportation, and the manufacture of hydrogen fuel cells, which may be the real answer for the future.

Outline

I. Petroleum comes from small marine plants raining to the bottom of the ocean, where they are preserved and buried in *reservoirs*, that is, rocks of high porosity and permeability, such as sandstone and limestone. A *cap rock*—the best is shale—sits over the reservoir, keeping the oil and gas inside.

   A. Keep in mind that the oil in this system is emulsified with water.

   B. For commercial production, the oil must be concentrated into a smaller volume. The structure that performs this function is a *trap*, such as an *anticlinal trap*. The oil migrates to the axial region of the anticline, where a well can be drilled.

II. Seventy percent of the U.S. energy budget is oil-based.

   A. Most of the known oil reserves are in the Middle East. The United States owns about 5% of the rest of the world's oil reserves.

   B. The United States consumes about 30% of all the oil produced in the world and imports about 51% of all the oil it uses.

C. When the United States supported Israel during the 1973 war with its Arab neighbors, the members of the Organization of the Petroleum Exporting Countries (OPEC), which is dominated by the countries of the Middle East, imposed an oil embargo on our country. A crisis was precipitated in the United States, eventually causing Americans to lower their demand for oil. With the reduction in demand, the embargo was lifted.

D. The obvious problem at that time was the large size and gas inefficiency of American cars. When Japan provided an answer by exporting more efficient cars to the United States, the American car industry followed suit and began to manufacture more efficient cars. But memories are short, and American cars have become larger.

E. In 1952, at a meeting of the American Association of Petroleum Geologists, M. King Hubbert warned about the overproduction of non-renewable resources.
   1. Hubbert predicted that American oil wells would peak out (both in production and discovery) in the 1960s. In fact, domestic production peaked in 1968.
   2. Hubbert also predicted that worldwide production would peak somewhere around the turn of the 21st century.
   3. Although highly unpopular and rejected at the time, Hubbert's predictions are now proving to be true. It has been estimated that worldwide production will peak in about 2010.
   4. Hubbert also predicted that there would not be enough oil left anywhere in the world to even bother to look for it by 2100.

III. What can we do in the United States?
   A. According to Charles Mankin, former director of the Sarkeys Energy Center at the University of Oklahoma, Americans can reduce imports by eliminating the need for gas, not diesel. Then, the United States would have enough oil to be self-sufficient.

   B. One way to do this would be to start producing ethanol, as has been done in Brazil. In Brazil, ethanol is made from sugar cane. In the United States, ethanol could be made from corn.

1. Cars can run on ethanol.
2. Cars can also run on liquefied natural gas. This began to be made a few years ago, but the trend did not last.

C. The future appears to be in hydrogen. The hydrogen fuel cell is currently being developed. Its first use was in the Apollo Project to the Moon.
   1. Although one hydrogen cell does not have much power, hydrogen cells can be made in any size.
   2. To make a hydrogen cell, hydrogen gas and oxygen are brought together. They run into a catalyst, which strips the electrons off the hydrogen anions to make ions. A film allows the hydrogen ions to pass through to the other side of the cell, but the electrons cannot get through. The electrons follow a wire (creating an electric charge) to reach the other side of the cell and react with oxygen to form water.
   3. Jonathan Rifkin, author of *The Hydrogen Economy*, advised using renewable sources of electricity (for example, solar and wind sources) to make hydrogen cells.

Recommended Reading:

Edwards, John D., "Crude Oil and Alternate Energy Production Forecasts for the Twenty-First Century: The End of the Hydrocarbon Era."

Questions to Consider:

1. According to recent estimates, will the finding of new petroleum deposits significantly prolong the availability of petroleum as a major world energy source?
2. What appears to be the best potential way for the world to wean itself of its need for oil?

Lecture Thirty-Six—Transcript
Economic Geology of Petroleum

In this lecture, we're going to talk about petroleum. Petroleum represents 70% of the total energy budget of this country, and this is especially why I think everybody ought to know something about it. First of all, let's talk about the source of this stuff. Where does it come from? It comes from plants, again. And the difference between coal, which comes from plants, too, and petroleum, which comes from plants, is that these plants are marine plants. Now, when people think of marine plants, I guess they think of kelp, and seaweed, and all that. And I suppose that would contribute to it, too. But most of the plants we're talking about are the ones that are up there in that plankton that rain to the ocean bottom constantly, all the time.

Now, again, if you're going to preserve this stuff, you've got to keep it away from oxygen and microbial activity. And the fact of the matter is there are areas of the ocean bottom that, indeed, do that, and I won't bore you with what they're all about. So the idea is somewhere on the ocean bottom we do preserve this stuff—and then we bury it. And then again, it goes through one of these transformations that nobody really understands: Once again, unless you can do it in a laboratory, you really can't understand what's going on. So what exactly the chemistry is in the transformation from green plants out in the ocean to petroleum, I really don't know.

Once you have it, though, you've got to keep it somewhere, and where we keep it is in rocks that we call *reservoirs*. Well, the reservoirs have all the same attributes as the aquifers we talked about: high porosity, high permeability. So everything you learned about aquifers is directly applicable here. So when you consider different kinds of reservoirs, think of the aquifers we talked about. The absolute number one aquifer was sandstones. Well, the same thing is true here. Most of the petroleum that has been produced over the long haul of time has come out of sandstone reservoirs. And the number two is limestones. After that, there really isn't much in the way of reservoirs. I don't know, for example, of any commercial field that would produce oil or gas, and, let's say, weathered igneous rocks. So it's pretty much those two.

Now, once you have it, now, in this reservoir, you've got to keep it in the reservoir. Remember, we're talking about liquids now, and gasses especially, very easy to escape. So what you have to have over top of this reservoir is what we call a *cap rock*. And it should come as no surprise to find out the very, very best cap rock is a shale in a very low porosity and permeability. So the perfect scenario, then, would be a sandstone or a limestone reservoir capped with this layer of shale. Now, here's a point, though. People sort of visualize when they hear that, that here within this layer of rock, the oil or the gas is simply moving through. But that's not exactly true. This is still an aquifer. What's moving through the rock is still water mostly. The oil is emulsified with the water; the gas is dissolved in it.

And so if you want to have a commercial production somewhere, what you have to do is to concentrate the oil or gas in a smaller volume to the point where it's economically feasible to produce. And the structure that does that—there are a number of them—but we call that a *trap* And there are different kinds of traps, but the one that has produced the most oil and gas over the long haul of the industry has been the anticlinal trap: remember, where you fold rocks up into an anticline? If there's any oil or gas around, it will migrate to the axial region of the anticline and accumulate. And then all you have to do is find that axis, get a well drilled into it, and you're in business. I have to point out that the person who first suggested the trap was a Morgantonian—would you believe, a Morgantonian—by the name of I. C. White. Anyway, so once you have that now, you can be in business.

Now, what I really want to talk about mainly in this presentation are some of the problems we are facing—and will face increasingly into the future—with our dependence upon petroleum. First of all, one of the problems, I think, is the fact that we depend upon it so heavily. We're talking 70% of our total energy picture is in that one source. It just seems to me that putting your eggs all in one basket like that isn't too terribly bright, but we have indeed done that. So, 70% of all of our energy comes from petroleum, mostly oil. Then I think the other problem is where the remaining oil is. Well, I think, you look around the world, and you'll find out—and I think most people know this—most of the remaining oil in the world is in the Middle East. Something over half of all the oil is in the Middle East, and I think you have to say it's a rather a tumultuous part of the world. And if you go into the Middle East, the question is who has the most? Well, Saudi Arabia has about 25% of all the remaining oil in the world.

Kuwait is right behind her with about maybe 10% or 11%—the numbers may change from time to time. Right after that is Iran and Iraq with about 10% each. And then after that, the remainder of the 50+% would be any number of the emirates around the Persian Gulf. So that's where most of it is.

Here's the real question though: How much do we have? Well, here we are—the United States, we own about 5% of the remaining oil of the world, which I think is kind of fair because here we are roughly 5% of the world's population. But here is the problem: In this country it is estimated that we consume within our borders 30% of all the oil produced in the world. Now, I think you can see right off the bat that's going to be somewhat of a problem somewhere down the line, 30%. Obviously, we do not produce anywhere near what we need ourselves, and so what we do is we import. The last figure I saw was that we imported about 51% of all the oil we use. Now, note: That's saying over half of all the energy we generate from petroleum, we generate from petroleum brought into the country from outside. Well, again, this is a problem. You're depending upon someone else to provide over half of your energy source in terms of petroleum. And the other one—I'm not an economist, but it would seem to me that another problem is the fact that you're shipping money overseas to buy oil that you could be spending within the United States for other things that we need. So, I think you can see some real problems right there in just where it is and how much we've got.

But another problem—let me sort of set the scene for this one, and a lot of you will remember this. Back in the '70s, we were importing at that time about 40% of all of our oil, and at that time, almost all of it was coming from the Middle East, forty-some %. Then what happened? There was a war between Israel and her Arab neighbors, and the federal government of the United States supported Israel, and it angered the Arab countries, for good reason, and OPEC. OPEC—now, you all know, I think, is the Organization of Petroleum Exporting Countries. These are countries that produce more oil than they need themselves, so what they do is they sell it to other people, like the United States, who don't have all they need.

Well, OPEC, as you might see, is really ruled by the Arab countries—so right off the bat they put an embargo on us. They said, "We're not going to sell you any more oil." Now, here's the problem—here's what most people don't know, and I think this is very, very important. Every drop of oil that's brought into this country, then and now, every drop of imported oil is used to make two materials: one, gasoline, and two, diesel fuel. Now, for those of you who heat your home with oil, that's also the same as number five: oil. But gasoline and diesel. All of a sudden, literally overnight, the supplies of gasoline and diesel just started to plummet. Well, you remember, then, those long lines at the gas station, waiting to get your car filled up with gas. Now, in Morgantown it wasn't so bad because we're not a terribly big town. But still we would sit in line for a half an hour, 40 minutes, 45 minutes to get up to the tank to get filled up. But you remember reading from big cities about people standing in line for hours trying to get up to the pump to get their cars filled up with gasoline. And then it got so bad that they would only give you 10 gallons—they wouldn't even fill your tanks. So that meant you had to sit in line for two or three times if you wanted to fill your tank up with gasoline. Well, it just got to the point where you just didn't drive anywhere. You never knew if you were going to have enough fuel to get back from wherever you were going—so people stopped driving places, and it became really, really, really nasty.

The really bad problem besides that, of course, was here diesel was going down the tubes, too, and, of course, think about diesel now. What does diesel run? It runs the railroads, and it runs trucking. So all of a sudden, for example, I can remember in Morgantown things happening like groceries or produce started to disappear. Why? Most of the produce we have is coming in from places like California or Florida by train, and then it is distributed into towns by truck. Well, all of a sudden the amount of diesel fuel made available to these people who were trucking things of any kind was dropping. So it became a very, very bad scenario. And on top of that, they were really worried about the fact that in the upcoming winter there wouldn't be enough number five oil, same as diesel, to heat people's homes—especially in places like New England, where they depend upon it a lot. And then the problem was in these places if the homes are cooling off, old people might get chilled, and, as a result, die. And it was just a bad, bad scene.

And then we did something that OPEC never thought we would do—we started to conserve. You see, the United States has never been very conservative-minded. We don't save anything because we've always been too rich—but we started to conserve. For example, people started carpooling. It was pretty rare to see a car with one person in it. A lot of people just put their cars away, and they started taking public transportation—if it was available. They started bicycling to work. They started walking to work. I walked to work I only live about 2½ miles from my office, so I started walking to work. All of a sudden the demand for gasoline just flattened right out. And then, I think, that probably scared OPEC because they probably thought, "Well, if we finally lift the embargo maybe they won't even want our oil anymore." So they lifted it. And everything sort of, kind of, returned to normal.

But the problem was pretty apparent. The problem was so obvious: It was the car. The American car if you think back to the '70s, it was huge. I mean, we're talking huge: big fins and all that stuff—huge engines, very poor gas mileage. I mean, if you got 10 miles to a gallon out of one of these cars, you were doing very, very well. All of a sudden, that was the problem. Can we fix that problem? Well, I can remember reading about the people going to Detroit and saying, "How about giving us smaller cars and more efficient engines?" And of course, Detroit said, "No." Why? I guess they said, "No" because they weren't going to make as much money on a little car as they made on a big one. But they said "No" anyway. And then in the background we heard, "You people want small cars? We've got small cars." And of course, you know who that was—Japan. That's when all the Japanese imports started.

Well, at long last, Detroit finally woke up, and they finally started making smaller cars, and they did improve the efficiency of the engine. For example, the old engines used to use carburetion, remember that—the carburetors? Now, there's no carburetion anymore. It's all fuel injection. It's all computer controlled. So, the automobile engine of today is not anything like it was back in the '70s. It is really a very, very efficient machine. It can get better, and I think it will get better in the future.

But here as I look back on all this now—even my generation, who lived through this, you know thoughts fade. And all of a sudden, people start forgetting those long lines at gas stations. And what's happening now? The cars are getting bigger again, and the engines are getting bigger again, and they're very fuel efficient, you see—but they're still bigger, and they're demanding more, and more, and more of that fuel. So, anyway, I think we've got to think about that. Do we need big cars like that? Do we need these huge engines like that? Well, that's something someone has to come to grips with and decide. But that's not the real problem.

Let me tell you now what I consider to be the real problem involved here. Back in, let's see, it was 1952, there was a talk given at the National Meeting of the American Association of Petroleum Geologists, now, the AAPG is probably the biggest organization of its kind in the world. And this is not just for geologists. This is anybody who works in the petroleum industry: The geologists, the engineers, even the company people—everybody belongs to the AAPG. There was a guy by the name of M. King Hubbert. M. King Hubbert was giving a talk to the AAPG, and he was talking to them about non-renewable resources. Now, we talked about this before, so you know what they are. But here's what he was demonstrating to them: He demonstrated that if you were to plot discovery and production of anything versus time, if it's a non-renewable resource, the distribution would be a perfect Gaussian distribution. In other words, whatever this stuff is, we sort of discover it, and then we say, "Yeah, we really like that. Won't you go out and find some more?" So then you're out there looking for the very-easy-to-find rich deposits of whatever this is. And as time goes on, the deposits are becoming smaller and not quite so rich. And then they're becoming increasing difficult to find. And pretty soon they're getting really kind of scarce. And pretty soon that's it. I don't care what this non-renewable resource is—they're all going to have that same curve.

Well, he was talking to them, and he said, "Okay, let's take a look at this scenario now." When did all this industry start? Well, it turns out, if you look at the industry as we know it today, it really started in about 1859 with a well drilled just south of Erie, Pennsylvania, called *Titusville*. So he put that date down at the beginning of this thing, and then he started making predictions. One of the predictions he made was—this was 1952 now—he made the prediction that at the rate we were consuming oil in this country that we would reach a maximum peak out in domestic production and discovery of our own oil somewhere around the end of the '60s, early '70s. Well, the best I can find out looking at the literature is that we probably peaked out somewhere around 1968. So that means for 40 years now, we've been on the backside of this curve. Well, if you mention that to somebody, they'll say, "Yeah, but we're still discovering things." Yeah, we still are discovering places—we're discovering new oil and gas deposits. But they're not very big, and they're not enough to provide us all that we need, you see. So, anyway, then somebody brings up (always, of course) the North Slope of Alaska—Prudhoe Bay and all that. Well, that's pretty good. Prudhoe Bay, the North Slope of Alaska, was without a doubt the biggest oil find ever in North America. There was no find ever as large as Prudhoe Bay— but here's the problem with Prudhoe Bay. The problem with Prudhoe Bay is that every field has a curve like that. It sputted in, they say, it sputted in, and then it peaks out, and then finally you drain it. Well, it just so happens that Prudhoe Bay peaked out in about 1985. So you see, we're way on the backside of that curve, too. So, anyway, they didn't want to hear that kind of stuff, but he was telling them, "We better start thinking about the fact that we're using our oil in this country too fast. We should start conserving this thing. We should start doing things that are going to reduce the demand of oil in our country." Well, of course, they didn't want to hear that because they were in the business of selling it, I guess.

Then he came up with another prediction. The next prediction is one they really, really didn't want to hear. He predicted in 1952, that world production—we're talking a non-renewable resource here— world production, he predicted in 1952, as he put it, "would peak out somewhere around the turn of the century." That's what he said. Well, the turn of the century in 1952 was a half a century away, and you know what predictions are like that. Half a century away—forget it, that's a long way off. But they really didn't want to hear that at all. But anyway, they really badmouthed M. King Hubbert. They called him a crazy man. They said he was uninformed, he didn't know what he was talking about. They just would not believe it.

Well, it turns out that about three years ago, I think it was, an article appeared in the bulletin, now, of the AAPG, and this article basically evaluated the world scenario. And the end product, or the summary of all this: They finally concluded that remember that prediction that M. King Hubbert made, that the world production would peak out around the year 2000? Well, he was wrong. They predicted that world production would peak out in the year 2010. 2010? That's basically where we are. 2010. And this is company people now. So, the idea now, is—even amongst those who know—they realize that the world production of petroleum is going to peak out very, very soon, and then we're going to be on that backward slide for the world. Well, then all the other numbers he predicted probably will hold true. For example, he predicted by the year 2050, there wouldn't be enough oil produced in the world to be a major energy source for any major country like the United States, like Europe, like Canada. Here we have China coming on board now, you see, that's a real scare. All of a sudden, the Chinese are starting to have cars of their own, and they're demanding—or going to demand—large amounts of petroleum.

All of a sudden this is a big problem now. What are we going to do in the year 2050 for petroleum? Now, I'm not really concerned an awful lot, I guess, because I'm going to be in that big reservoir in the sky. But our children are going to be here. Our grandchildren are going to be here. What are they going to do in the year 2050 for an energy source? They're going to have to be looking for something other than petroleum because there's not going to be much of that left. Then he predicted that by the year 2100—in 2100, he said "There won't be enough oil in the ground to even go out and bother looking for it anymore." That's amazing—do you know what that says? In 1859 to 2100, what is that 250 years? In 250 years, we'll have consumed in this country the amount of oil it took Mom Nature 600 million to 700 million years to make. That's a long time. And it's going to be gone.

I think somebody better start thinking about this. Is there anything we can do? There's nothing we can do about that curve. That's cast in iron—that's like granite carvings, you see, you're not going to do anything about that one. But is there something we can do? Well, yeah, I think so. We can probably go back and look at that import business. Remember now, the stuff we import is used to make two things: gasoline and diesel. There was a guy by the name of Charlie Mankin. Charlie Mankin was the director of the Oklahoma Survey until he retired a number of years ago. Charlie Mankin was an expert, a recognized expert, in petroleum—in petroleum energy of all kinds. And, of course, being from Oklahoma, they're right in the middle of all this. Charlie Mankin gave us a talk at the university, and he made some interesting comments. It was his opinion that if we would just eliminate the need for gasoline—forget about the diesel now—just eliminate the need for gasoline, he said that we probably have within our borders enough oil to provide everything else we need at least for awhile. In other words, we're still going to run out now, understand that. But all I'm saying is, he said that if we could eliminate the need for gasoline, his comment was, "We wouldn't even have to import any oil." And that's the point. If we eliminated the need for gasoline, we don't have to import any oil anymore.

Question is: Can we do that? Well, yeah. I mean, you hear about it a lot, and it's becoming more and more prevalent in the papers and on TV: ethanol, for example—that's the last big thing. Ethanol—will your car and mine burn ethanol? Sure, it will. It's not a bad fuel at all. And they're talking now about making ethanol out of all the corn we generate out in the Midwest. Yeah, let's use ethanol. For example, the country of Brazil has converted over 100% to an ethanol-based fuel—and as a result of that, they stopped importing oil. The country of Brazil, now, has cut themselves off totally from the oil market. They don't need it anymore. They are self-sufficient in fuel because they are making this ethanol out of their sugar cane, something they produce a lot. Well, we produce a lot of corn. Why can't we do the same thing? Well, I think you're going to find that this is going to become more and more of an issue. Should we or should we not? There are always pros and cons. But know, this gasohol thing has been around for a long time. So I think there's a real possibility. We've got to come up with something. There's something that's already been tested. Our cars will run on ethanol.

Something else, and this was something that Charlie suggested, too. And I had never thought of this, but after he said it, of course, hindsight's a great thing. Liquified natural gas—you know when it comes to natural gas, I don't know if anybody really knows how much natural gas is out there. We've got pretty good estimates on how much oil there is. How much natural gas, however, I'm not sure anybody really knows. When they had these estimates, the numbers are so big that I can't even comprehend them. So, anyway, here was his comment—now, when we're drilling for oil, for example, more times than not, they run into natural gas, and they just flare it off. No, don't do that. Collect every bit we can. Liquify it. Put it under pressure and liquify it. As a matter of fact, I just saw in the news the other day, we're talking about oil tankers. They're now building liquified natural gas tankers: shipping liquid natural gas across the oceans. Liquified natural gas is a great, great, fuel. Will your car and mine run on it? Absolutely it will. As a matter of fact, there have been a number of cases where they have built these things—and I think Detroit must have because I remember some of these cars on the road that were built with a tank for liquified natural gas and one for gasoline. The idea is if you were in a place where you could buy liquified natural gas, you did. Why? It was cheaper—by a lot, a lot cheaper than gasoline. But if you weren't, you bought gasoline. But the thing is as you're driving along and you run out of one, you just flip the switch, the engine changes over to the other—it's just a little tweak of the computer, you see.

So, liquified natural gas. For example, at the university, over half, I think, of all the physical plant vehicles that run around the university—those are all liquified natural gas. And about 10 years ago, this seemed to be catching on. You know, the problem was where are you going to buy this stuff? Well, about 10 years ago there seemed to be enough of these cars on the road with liquified natural gas tanks and gasoline that it paid. A few stations—for example, in Morgantown there were three stations that opened up selling liquified natural gas. It looked like we were going in that direction. And then something happened. And I'm not sure what it was. I asked one of the owners, "What happened?" because he stopped selling it. He said, "I really don't know what happened. All I know is there were fewer and fewer customers for it, and it was expensive to keep it because you had to keep it under pressure." So now, for example, there are no liquified natural gas stations in the city of Morgantown.

So here's what he suggested. I think this is a good one. Just picture the following. If everyone would contact their congressman, their representative, their senator, and say, "You know that liquified natural gas that was going for awhile? You guys start thinking about that again." Just think what would happen if the government would say as of January of next year, all government vehicles that now run on gasoline will run on liquified natural gas. Do you know how many vehicles that is? I mean, it's got to be a gazillion. I mean, just think of all those little white things that deliver the mail. I don't even know how many of those there are—so, anyway, that's something to think about, liquified natural gas. I think that will help us a lot to get us away from petroleum. Now, not entirely—it's still sort of a petroleum product, but we'll get away from that imported oil.

But the last one I want to comment on—I think this is coming to the fore, and I've read a lot about this, and it seems to be the future, as far as my interpretation—hydrogen: hydrogen as a fuel. Now, people are afraid of hydrogen because they remember the Hindenburg. Forget the Hindenburg. Well, you want to remember it? Remember the Hindenburg went up, and all the flames went vertically? That's the reason why so many people were able to escape from the Hindenburg: because the flames went up. Just think if you have a wreck out on the road: impact, gasoline on the road, and the flames. I'd rather have a hydrogen tank in the back of my car, I think, than have a gasoline tank. But anyway—hydrogen. We talk about the hydrogen fuel cell—that's the big thing now, and if you want to learn something about that one, just Google it. I mean, there are all kinds of information on the Internet. But anyway, hydrogen fuel cell—I was surprised to find out this is not a new invention. I think it was invented way back in the early 1800s. It was never used. It was sort of a toy that the physicists had. The first use of the hydrogen fuel cell was sending the troops to the moon, the Apollo project, that's how they generated their fuel: hydrogen fuel cells.

Here's the way it works, very simple. You have this cell. You bring hydrogen gas in on one side, oxygen—or you can use the air because it's 21% oxygen. Then it runs into what we call a *catalyst*, and what the catalyst does, it strips the electrons off the hydrogen anions to make them ions now. Now, you've got hydrogen ions and electrons. Then there's a film that only allows positive things to go through. The hydrogen ions go through to the other side of the cell. The electrons can't get through. How do they get over there? They go up and follow a wire. Electrons following the wire—that's an electric charge, you see. Then on the other side, they get back together again, and they react with oxygen, and form water. That's the end product. It's as simple as that. Now, any one little fuel cell doesn't produce an awful lot of power. But you just stack them together just like the battery in your car. The fuel cell to drive a car—every manufacturer is working on these things—is about the size of a carry-on bag. I'm sure they'll get smaller and smaller as time goes on, and cheaper. Right now they're very expensive. But you see, that's just a question of production: The more you make, the cheaper they'll get.

Here's the point about hydrogen fuel cells. You can make them in any size you want. You can make them to drive your car. You can make one big enough to provide all the power you need for your house, and note: You don't have to be connected to that big power plant down the road. You can make them any size at all. There's a book out you might be interested in. It's called *The Hydrogen Economy*. It was written by a guy by the name of Jeremy Rifkin. At the time of the writing, I think he was on the staff of the Wharton School of Finance. Get it. It talks about using hydrogen as a worldwide, now, source of energy. Where are you going to get it? Well, his idea is you make water, and you dissociate it with electrodes, and you've probably done it as an experiment somewhere. You need a lot of electricity, but here's his comment: "Use renewable types of energy to make the electricity. Use solar power where you've got it. Use the wind. Burn biomass." That's how you make the electricity. Use those kinds of things, which always are renewable. Generate the hydrogen, pipe it to people's homes, send it to people's homes, and send it to gas stations. And that's his whole idea. This is the world's source, now, for an energy supply. And note: We're talking here about eliminating everything except hydrogen.

Well, my time is coming to an end. I have tried in these lectures to give you some fundamental ideas and understanding of geology, and chemistry as a matter of fact. We've talked about all of the major areas of geology, and I've tried to give you enough information— obviously we couldn't get into great detail. But I think what we have talked about in all the different areas—weathering, soil development, erosion—that you can understand what we're talking about. And best of all, you can understand and see what's around you. And I will go back to the statement I made in the very, very first lecture. My total reason for doing a class like this, and my total reason for going into any classroom, is to have the people take away what they learn from me everywhere they go for the rest of their lives, and look around at the world around you with a little bit different understanding and appreciation.

Timeline

B.C.

13.7 billion years ago	Big Bang—origin of the universe
4.5 billion years ago	Creation of planet Earth from protoplanet Earth
3.9–4.2 billion years ago	Oldest crustal rocks
3.6 billion years ago	First bona fide evidence of life (blue-green algae)
2.5 billion years ago	Modern rate of plate tectonics thought to begin
1.0 billion years ago	Formation of Rodinia, the supercontinent that preceded Pangea
800–700 million years ago	First large soft-bodied animals
550 million years ago	First shelled animals
300 million years ago	Creation of supercontinent of Pangea
200 million years ago	Breakup of Pangea—creation of modern continents
60 million years ago	Extinction of dinosaurs
2 million years ago	Onset of Northern Hemisphere continental glaciation

A.D.

1785	James Hutton publishes his *Theory of Earth*
1830	Charles Lyell publishes the first real geology text, *Principles of Geology*
1857	James Hall theorizes geosyncline
1859	Charles Darwin publishes *Origin of Species*

1896	Pierre and Marie Curie and H. Becquerel discover radioactivity
1902	E. Rutherford and F. Soddy establish radioactive dating
1915	Alfred Wegener proposes supercontinent of Pangea and its breakup to form the modern continents
1947	W. F. Libby establishes carbon-14 dating
1963	Vine and Matthews document the concept of the sea floor spreading with their discovery of magnetic zonation of the oceanic crust
Mid-1960s	Originally recognized in the 1920s by a German seismologist, Beno Gutenberg, his discovery of the asthenosphere was viewed with great skepticism until the 1960s
Mid-1960s	Establishment of the theory of plate tectonics

Glossary

aa: The Hawaiian term for basaltic lava characterized by a rough, jagged surface.

abrasion: The process whereby rock surfaces are worn away by the frictional contact of rock particles transported by wind, running water, waves, glacial ice, or gravity.

abyssal plain: The perfectly flat, deepest portion of the ocean bottom beyond the continental rise.

Acadian orogeny: The orogenic event that affected the northern Appalachians during the Devonian period.

accretionary wedge: A mixture of materials stripped from the descending lithospheric plate that is accreted to the edge of the overlying plate.

acid mine drainage: The acidic iron- and sulfate-rich water that is commonly associated with the mining of materials containing pyrite.

acid soil: The soil typical of humid, temperate climates, in which the cation exchange positions have been hydrogenated by percolating acidic rainwater.

active volcano: Any volcano that shows some indication that the associated magma is molten.

agricultural lime: Powdered limestone that is used to neutralize acidic soils.

Alleghenian orogeny: The final orogeny that created the structures seen throughout the present-day Appalachians and that completed the formation of Pangea.

alluvial fan: The gently sloping, fan-shaped deposit that accumulates where a mountain stream flows out onto an adjoining basin, particularly in arid and semiarid regions.

alpine glacier: A glacier confined to a mountain valley.

amino acids: Complex organic molecules that are the basis for the development of life.

amplitude: The distance from the crest of a wave to the bottom of the adjoining trough. In the case of folds, the distance between the crest of the anticline to the bottom of the adjacent syncline.

angle of repose: The angle above which loose material will begin to move downslope.

anion: An atom or group of atoms that possesses a negative charge because of an excess number of electrons.

anticline: A convex upward fold in which the oldest rocks are located in the center.

aphelion: The point in the orbit of a solar system object where it is farthest from the Sun.

aquiclude: An impermeable rock or unconsolidated deposit that is incapable of allowing the passage of water.

aquifer: A rock or an unconsolidated deposit with sufficient porosity and permeability to conduct significant volumes of water to a well or spring.

aquitarde: A semipermeable rock or unconsolidated deposit that does not readily conduct water to a well or spring.

arete: A knife-edged mountain ridge created by alpine glaciation.

aridosol: Alkaline or saline soils that develop under arid conditions.

arkose: A sandstone of continental origin containing at least 25% feldspar.

artesian well: Any well producing water from a confined aquifer.

ash: Pyroclastic materials with diameters of less that 2.0 mm generated during volcanic eruptions.

asteroids: Any of a number of relatively small celestial bodies that orbit the Sun, mostly between the orbits of Mars and Jupiter.

asthenosphere: Part of the upper mantle immediately below the lithosphere that is characterized by a plastic response to stress.

asymmetric fold: A fold whose limbs dip in opposite directions at different angles.

atom: The neutral system of negatively charged electrons moving around a dense, positively charged nucleus.

atomic mass: The sum of the number of protons and neutrons in the nucleus of an atom.

atomic number: The number of protons in the nucleus of an atom.

axial plane: An imaginary plane that attempts to divide the cross-section of a fold into two equal halves.

back-arc basin: A basin, such as the Sea of Japan, that forms between a chain of island-arc volcanoes and the mainland, resulting from the rifting of the ocean floor.

bajada: A series of overlapping alluvial fans along the base of a mountain range.

Barringer Crater: The most recent impact crater on Earth, located in northeastern Arizona.

basalt: A fine-grained, dark-colored, extrusive igneous rock composed primarily of calcic plagioclase and pyroxenes.

base level: The surface down to which a stream is attempting to carve its channel.

Basin and Range Province: A geologic province centered over Nevada that is characterized by north-south–trending block-fault mountains.

batholith: A massive, intrusive igneous body with a surface exposure of greater than 40 square miles.

bauxite: The primary ore of aluminum, essentially hydrated alumina, $Al_2O_3 \cdot 2H_2O$.

bed load: That portion of a stream's load being carried along the bottom of the stream channel.

Big Bang: The theoretical explosion that initiated the formation and expansion of the Universe.

biochemical sedimentary rock: A sedimentary rock composed of materials generated by organisms.

black hole: An object that has collapsed under its own gravitation to such a small radius that its gravitational force traps photons of light.

block-fault mountain: Linear mountain ranges formed under tensional forces bounded on both sides by normal faults.

body wave: The seismic waves that travel through Earth.

bolson: An alluvium-covered basin into which drainage from adjacent mountains flows.

bomb: An aerodynamically shaped pyroclastic rock greater than 64 mm in diameter formed by the midair solidification of molten lava.

Bowen's crystallization series: An order of crystallization of silicate minerals from the cooling of molten magma or lava.

breccia: A sedimentary rock composed primarily of angular, granule-sized or larger rock fragments.

brittle strain: The response of a material when, once the elastic limit has been exceeded, the material breaks.

caldera: A large basin-shaped volcanic depression that is produced by the collapse of the overlying cone into an empty or partially empty magma chamber.

caliche: A mixture of sand, gravel, or desert debris cemented with porous calcium carbonate.

capacity: The total amount of load that a stream can carry.

carbonaceous chrondite: A meteorite containing chrondules having a high abundance of carbon and other volatile elements.

carbonation: Any reaction involving carbonic acid.

carbonation/hydrolysis: The major process whereby most rock-forming silicate minerals undergo chemical weathering that involves a reaction with carbonic acid (carbonation) and water (hydrolysis).

cation: A positively charged ion.

cation adsorption: The process whereby clay mineral particles neutralize their negative charges.

cation exchange: The process whereby positive ions in cation-adsorption sites can be replaced by other cations present in the soil water.

cave and cavern: Underground passageways created by the groundwater dissolution of limestone.

cementation: A process whereby loose sediments are converted into sedimentary rocks by minerals precipitating from groundwater solution into the pore spaces between the grains.

chemical atomic weight: The weighted average mass of the isotopes making up an element.

chemical sedimentary rock: A sedimentary rock consisting of non-clastic materials that were not generated by organisms.

chemical weathering: Any process whereby a mineral or rock is partially or totally decomposed.

chernozem: A Russian word meaning "black soil," in reference to the black color of mollisols.

chert: A sedimentary rock consisting of crypto-crystalline quartz.

chrondrite: A stony meteorite containing chrondrules.

chrondrule: A spherical inclusion in certain meteorites, usually composed of silicates.

cinder cone: A cone of loose cinders that accumulates around a volcanic fissure or vent.

cinders: Uncemented fragmental volcanic ejecta ranging from 3 mm to 4 mm in diameter.

cirque: A bowl-shaped mountain depression that forms at the headwaters of an alpine glacier.

clastic: Fragments of rock that have been moved from their point of origin.

clay minerals: A group of hydrous aluminum silicates formed from the carbonation/hydration of most of the major rock-forming silicate minerals. They are the major component of soil.

climate: The conditions of temperature and precipitation that exist for a long period of time in any region.

closed universe: According to theory, a universe that will eventually collapse back to the original primeval atom or singularity.

cohesion and friction: The two forces that resist the movement of loose materials on slopes.

col: A high mountain pass formed by the back-to-back intersection of two cirques.

collapse sinkhole: A sinkhole that forms when the roof of a cavern collapses either under its own weight or following the removal of weight-supporting groundwater.

columnar joint: Prismatic columns, commonly hexagonal cross-sections, that are found in basaltic rocks.

comet: A celestial body thought to be composed primarily of water ice that orbits the Sun in huge, highly elliptical patterns.

compaction: A process of lithification whereby clay-rich sediments are converted to rock by the physical exclusion of water. Shales and mudstones form by compaction.

compression: A force that acts toward a body and tends to reduce its volume and dimensions.

compression wave: A shock wave in which the particles of the propagating medium move back and forth in the direction of propagation.

cone of depression: The conical depression of the water table around a pumped water well.

confined aquifer: An aquifer sandwiched between two aquicludes and within which the water is under pressure.

conglomerate: A sedimentary rock composed primarily of rounded, granule-sized and larger particles.

contact metamorphism: The processes of change that take place in a host rock because of the heat at contact with an intruding magma.

continent-continent collision: A major mountain-building episode resulting from the collision of two continents. The current collision of India and Asia is an example.

continental-arc volcano: The chain of volcanoes that forms on the edge of the continental plate overlying a zone of subduction.

continental crust: The granitic rocks that underlie the continents and range up to 45 miles thick under mountain ranges.

continental glacier: A glacier of considerable thickness that covers a large part of a continent, obscuring the topography of the underlying surface over an area of at least 20,000 square miles.

continental shelf: The upper surface of the geocline surface that extends from the shoreline to the continental slope. The shallow portion of the ocean, averaging about 600 feet at the outer edge.

convection cell: The pattern of heat-driven asthenospheric rocks in which the central heated portion rises and the cooling outer portion sinks.

convergent plate margin: A boundary where two lithospheric plates are moving toward each other.

core: The innermost portion of Earth, thought to be composed of a mixture of iron and nickel. The outer portion of the core is molten, while the center is possibly solid or a highly viscous liquid.

cosmic dust: The remains of former stars, consisting of bits and pieces of metals, minerals, rocks, and ices, that fill the cosmos.

covalent bond: The chemical bond in which atoms join by a sharing of their outermost electrons. The strongest of all chemical bonds.

crater: The circular to elliptical structure that occupies the summit of a volcano. The bowl-shaped depression formed by meteorite impact.

creep: The slow, continuous movement of regolith downslope under the force of gravity.

cross beds: Individual beds inclined at an angle to the main bed of a sedimentary rock.

crust: The outermost portion of Earth that consists of the oceanic and continental crusts.

dark matter: The unseen matter that occupies the space within galaxies.

deadman: Structural components of walls designed to prevent the toppling of the wall by creep.

decollment: Near-horizontal thrust faults that form where upper folded and faulted layers of sedimentary rock move over underlying rocks.

decomposition: Any weathering process whereby minerals and rocks are partially or totally changed in composition.

deep-focus earthquake: An earthquake whose focus is located from about 200 miles to 450 miles below Earth's surface.

deep-sea trench: A long, narrow depression on the ocean floor that forms along convergent plate margins.

desert pavement: The layer of granule-sized and larger particles covering the desert floor, produced by the preferential removal of sand-sized and smaller particles.

diatom: A single-celled plant that secretes a siliceous frustule.

dip: The angle that a structural plane, such as a fault or a bed, makes with the horizontal.

disintegration: The process by which rocks are physically reduced in particle size.

displacement: The actual amount of movement along a fault surface.

dissolution: The process by which a solid dissolves in a solvent.

dissolved load: That stream load that is carried in solution.

divergence: Refers to the movement of lithospheric plates away from each other.

divergent plate margin: The margin between diverging lithospheric plates at rift zones, rift valleys, linear oceans, and oceanic ridges.

domal mountain: Mountains created by the localized, vertical uplift of Earth's crust.

dormant volcano: A volcano that has not shown signs of activity in historic time, has been active in the past, and is expected to be active in the future.

double-chain silicate structure: The silicate structure in which two parallel chains of silicon tetrahedra are joined along their lengths.

drag fold: A minor fold, usually in incompetent beds, that forms on opposite sides of a fault by the movement of rocks.

dripstone: The common name given to the materials that form from the precipitation of calcite or other materials from water solution.

dry-based glacier: A glacier, usually in polar regions, that is frozen to the underlying bedrock.

dust: The smallest particle size visible to the unaided human eye.

dynamo-thermal metamorphism: A type of regional metamorphism involving high pressures, shearing stress, and heat.

earthquake intensity: The amount of damage incurred by an earthquake.

earthquake magnitude: The amount of movement involved in an earthquake. Magnitude is measured by the Richter scale.

ecliptic: The plane of Earth's orbit around the Sun.

elastic limit: The point beyond which a material can no longer absorb and store energy.

elastic strain: The type of strain in which the applied force is absorbed, stored during deformation, and released as the material returns to its original shape.

electron: A negatively charged fundamental particle.

energy level: Discrete level surrounding the nucleus of an atom within which the electrons reside.

epicenter: The point on Earth's surface immediately above the focus of an earthquake.

epiorogenic force: Vertically directed mountain-building force.

erosion: Any process whereby the products of weathering are picked up and carried away.

evaporite sedimentary rock: A sedimentary rock formed from materials that are so water soluble that the water must be evaporated before precipitation will commence.

exfoliation: Any process whereby concentric layers are removed from the surface of a rock.

exterior drainage: Drainage systems where the water eventually reaches the ocean.

extinct volcano: A volcano that is not active and is not likely to become active in the future.

fall: One of the three types of mass wasting requiring the least amount of involvement of water; in a fall, rocks are subjected to maximum Go Force and little or no Stay Force.

fault: A break in Earth's crust along which there has been movement.

ferromagnesian silicate mineral: Those silicate minerals containing appreciable amounts of iron and magnesium.

fire fountain: An eruptive feature in which basaltic magmas are blown into the air up to a few thousand feet and break into cinders that fall around the vent to form a cinder cone.

flat universe: The scenario in which the expansion may stop, but the Universe will never collapse.

flint: A type of chert used by paleo-people to fashion tools.

flood basalt: Horizontal to sub-horizontal flows of basaltic lava that issue from many fractures over a wide area.

floodplain: That portion of a stream valley adjacent to the stream that is constructed of sediments overlying the erosional valley flat.

flow: A type of mass wasting that involves major quantities of water that intermix with loose debris to form a material that has the properties of a liquid.

flyweight star: A star less than 0.5 solar masses.

focus: The point at which the energy of an earthquake is released.

fold: A bend in strata, usually in response to compressional forces.

fold axis: The line of intersection of a fold and the axial plane.

foldbelt mountain: A mountain range within which a significant portion consists of folded sedimentary rocks.

footwall: The mass of rock beneath a fault plane.

fossil: The remains or the impression of the remains of a once-living organism.

fracture: A break in a rock due to mechanical failure. The breaking of a mineral other than along cleavage plains.

framework silicate structure: The silicate structure characterized by a three-dimensional arrangement of tetrahedra, in which each oxygen is shared by an adjoining tetrahedron.

free-flowing artesian well: An artesian well that produces water above the surface of the ground.

frost heaving: The process whereby particles of soil are lifted by the growth of an underlying ice crystal.

frost wedging: A physical weathering process whereby rocks are split apart by the cyclic freezing and thawing of water in fractures.

fumarole: A volcanic vent that emits hot gases.

galaxy: A huge group of stars, planets, and other bodies in the Universe.

geocline: The wedge of sediment that accumulates at the margin of a continental trailing edge.

geosyncline: A regional downwarping of the continental margin.

geyser: A volcanic feature that cyclically emits hot water and steam.

Gondwana: The Late Paleozoic continent of the Southern Hemisphere consisting of the present-day continents of South America, Africa, Antarctica, Australia, and India.

graben: The downthrown block associated with block-fault mountains.

gradient: The slope of a stream channel.

granite: A coarse-grained igneous rock consisting primarily of orthoclase, quartz, and plagioclase feldspar with minor amounts of biotite and amphiboles.

granodiorite: A coarse-grained igneous rock similar in composition to granite except for containing less orthoclase. With granite, makes up the continental crust.

graywacke: A dark-gray sandstone consisting of poorly sorted, angular quartz and feldspar with a variety of rock fragments in a clayey matrix.

Go Force: A term used in this discussion for the downslope component of gravity.

ground moraine: Till deposited during the retreat of a glacier.

hanging wall: The mass of rock above a fault plane.

hardness: The ability of a mineral to resist scratching by another mineral.

Hawaiian phase: The phase of eruption intensity described as nothing but the quiet evolution of lava. Molten rock on Earth's surface or its solidified counterpart.

heavyweight star: A star having greater than 8 solar masses.

hematite: The major mineral of iron, Fe_2O_3.

horizon: A layer that develops in undisturbed soils.

horn: A sharp mountain peak sculpted by the combined efforts of several surrounding cirques.

horst: The upthrown block associated with block-fault mountains.

hot spot: A source of basaltic magma at the top of the asthenosphere; hot spots are associated with mantle plumes and can last for several millions of years.

hot spring: A spring emitting water heated either by the geothermal gradient or by an underlying magma.

hydrogen bond: The bonding that occurs when a hydrogen atom comes between two small, highly electronegative atoms, such as N, O, and F.

hydrologic cycle: The circular pattern by which water originates from the oceans, passes through the atmosphere to the land, and eventually returns to the oceans.

hydrolysis: Any chemical reaction involving water.

hydrothermal feature: Surface emissions of heated water or steam.

hydrothermal metamorphism: The metamorphic process whereby host rocks are altered by the reaction with water or gases derived from magma.

Iapetus Ocean: The ocean created by the breakup of the supercontinent of Rodinia.

igneous rock: Any rock formed from the cooling and solidification of molten rock.

inorganic: Refers to compounds in which carbon is not a major component.

interior drainage: Streams that originate and terminate within the continent.

intermediate-focus earthquake: An earthquake that occurs in a zone from about 40 miles to about 250 miles below Earth's surface.

ion: An atom or group of atoms that has become positively or negatively charged.

ionic bonding: The electrostatic attraction between oppositely charged ions.

iron meteorite: Meteorites consisting of iron with varying amounts of nickel.

island-arc volcano: A volcano associated with a zone of subduction that builds from the ocean floor between the deep-sea trench and the continental margin.

isolated tetrahedral silicate structure: A silicate structure in which the silicon tetrahedra are joined by other metal ions.

isotope: Atoms with the same atomic number but different atomic masses.

joint: A break in the crust along which there has been little or no movement.

Jovian planet: Any of the four large gassy planets that orbit the Sun.

karst topography: Irregular topography developed by the surface and groundwater dissolution of underlying soluble rock, usually limestone.

lahar: A mudflow associated with a volcanic eruption.

laminar flow: The type of fluid flow in which the individual molecules are visualized as moving along parallel, uninterfering paths.

laminar layer: A thin layer of water theorized to exist where the water meets the stream channel and within which the water moves by laminar flow.

lateral moraine: A low, ridge-like moraine carried on or deposited near the side of an alpine glacier.

lava: Molten rock on Earth's surface or its solidified counterpart.

lava lake: A lake of molten lava, usually basaltic, that accumulates in a summit crater or on the flanks of a shield volcano.

left-lateral strike-slip fault: A strike-slip fault where an observer standing on one block must turn to the left to find the same index locality on the opposite block.

lepton: A fundamental particle of which the electron is the stable form.

levee: A natural or artificial embankment along the bank of a stream that serves to confine the stream flow to the channel.

lightweight star: A star between 0.5 and 4 solar masses.

limb: The part of a fold between the axes of the anticline and the adjacent syncline.

limestone: A sedimentary rock consisting primarily of the mineral calcite, $CaCO_3$.

limonite: A generic term for hydrated iron oxides, $FeO(OH)$.

linear ocean: A flooded rift valley; an intermediate stage between a rift valley and an opening ocean.

lithification: Any process that converts loose sediment into a sedimentary rock.

lithosphere: The combination of the crust and the outer, brittle portion of the mantle.

load: The amount of material actually being carried by a stream.

Love wave: The surface seismic wave in which the movement of the ground is horizontal and perpendicular to the direction of propagation.

luster: The appearance of a mineral under reflected light.

magma: Molten rock below Earth's surface.

magnetic reversal: The change in the polarity of Earth's magnetic field.

magnetite: The magnetic iron mineral Fe_3O_4.

main sequence: The period of a star's lifetime during which it is converting hydrogen to helium in its core.

mantle: That portion of Earth between the top of the core and the bottom of the crust.

marginal sea: The semi-enclosed sea between an island arc and the mainland. An example is the Sea of Japan.

maturity: The stage in Davis's cycle in which deposition exceeds active erosion, the streams are of low gradient and meandering, and wide floodplains are being created between subdued hills.

meander: The sinuous pattern characteristic of streams that have progressed to the stage of maturity.

medial moraine: A moraine carried on or in the middle of an alpine glacier that results from the coalescence of two inner lateral moraines below the juncture of two alpine glaciers. Upon retreat of the glacier, the moraine is deposited in the middle of the valley.

melange: A mass of folded, faulted, and metamorphosed rock that forms at convergent plate margins as part of the accretionary wedge.

Mercalli/Rossi scale: A scale of relative earthquake damage.

metallic bond: A type of chemical bond in which the valence electrons are not confined to individual atoms but, rather, flow freely through the entire crystal structure.

metamorphism: The combined chemical, mineralogical, and structural changes that take place within a rock mass as a result of the application of heat, pressure, and chemically active fluids.

metasomatism: A hydrothermal metamorphic process in which the original minerals of a rock are partially or totally replaced with a new assemblage of minerals.

meteor: The streak of light created as a meteoroid plunges through Earth's atmosphere.

meteorite: A meteoroid that has survived the passage through Earth's atmosphere and has impacted Earth.

meteoroid: A small interplanetary body.

middleweight star: A star between 4 and 8 solar masses.

mineral cleavage: The breaking of a mineral along planes of weakness within its crystal structure.

mollisol: The soil order that develops in semiarid, temperate climates.

monocline: A localized steepening in an otherwise uniform dip.

moraine: A mound, ridge, or other landform consisting of till deposited directly by a glacier.

mud cracks: Shrinkage cracks that develop in fine-grained, unconsolidated deposits as a result of drying or freezing.

mudstone: A sedimentary rock similar in composition to a shale but without the fine lamination characteristic of shale.

Nebular hypothesis: The theory set forth in 1755 by Immanuel Kant proposing that our solar system formed from a cloud of interstellar cosmic dust and gas.

neutron: The subatomic particle located in the nucleus of an atom with no charge and a mass of 1 amu; it consists of two down quarks and one up quark (ddu).

neutron star: A very dense stellar remnant whose interior consists entirely of neutrons.

nomograph: A graph or chart reducing a mathematical formula so that its value can be read for any value assigned to the variables involved.

non-clastic: Refers to material or rocks formed from substances once in solution.

nonferromagnesian silicate mineral: Silicate minerals whose compositions do not include appreciable amounts of iron or magnesium, primarily the feldspars, quartz, and muscovite.

non-renewable resource: A material that, once harvested, will not be replaced by a newly created unit of the material within a reasonably short period of time, usually taken as a human lifetime.

non-rotational compression: Compression in which the forces act toward and directly opposite each other.

non-silicate mineral: Minerals whose anion is other than the silicate anion.

normal fault: A fault formed under tensional forces in which the hanging wall has moved down relative to the footwall.

nuée ardente: A highly heated mass of gas-charged lava ejected more or less horizontally from a vent or summit of a volcano onto the outer slope, where it flows swiftly downslope as an avalanche.

ocean-continent collision: The convergence of an oceanic and continental plate at a zone of subduction.

ocean-island arc-continent collision: A convergent plate movement whereby an oceanic plate converges on a plate occupied by a chain of island-arc volcanoes and a continent.

oceanic crust: That portion of the crust underlying the ocean basins, consisting of basaltic lava.

oceanic ridge: A volcanic mountain range arising from the abyssal sea floor at the divergent plate margins; the site of sea floor spreading as new oceanic lithosphere is being created at its summit.

octet rule: The rule states that atoms that are able to acquire eight electrons in the outermost energy level become chemically inert.

old age: The third and final stage of Davis's landscape evolution theory, in which the stream channel is very near the base level, the relief of the landscape is very low, the stream gradients are very low, meandering is extreme, and abundant abandoned meanders or oxbow lakes are present.

Oort cloud: The theoretical cloud of comets that surrounds the solar system at a distance of approximately two light years.

open universe: The scenario in which the Universe will continue to expand forever.

organic: Refers to materials in which carbon is a major component.

orogenic forces: The horizontal, compressive forces that are generated at convergent plate margins.

outwash plain: The well-sorted, stratified deposit of sand, gravels, and cobbles eroded and transported from the terminal moraine of a continental glacier by meltwater streams.

overturned fold: A fold where both limbs dip in the same direction.

oxbow lake: A water-filled abandoned meander that is characteristic of stream valleys in Davis's landscape evolution stage of old age.

oxidation: Any reaction with oxygen.

oxisol: The soil order that forms in ever-hot, ever-wet tropical climates, consisting of a mixture of iron, aluminum, and silicon oxides.

pahoehoe: The Hawaiian term for a type of basaltic lava characterized by a smooth, ropey surface.

Pangea: The supercontinent proposed by Alfred Wegener that broke up about 200 million years ago to create the modern continents.

pedalfer: Acidic soils that form in humid, temperate climates under forest cover. In the United States, the term *pedalfer* has been superceded with the spodosol and ultisol soil orders.

pedocal: Neutral to alkaline soils that form under semiarid, temperate climates. In the United States, the term *pedocal* has been superceded by the mollisol order.

pedology: The scientific study of soils.

Pelean phase: A violent phase of volcanic eruption involving large volumes of pyroclastic material as well as a *nuée ardente*.

perched water table: The water table associated with a mass of groundwater isolated above the main body of groundwater by an impermeable layer of rock. Also referred to as a hanging water table.

peridotite: A coarse-grained, ultra-mafic igneous rock, consisting primarily of olivine, that makes up the upper portion of the mantle.

perihelion: The point in the orbit of any Sun-orbiting body where it most closely approaches the Sun.

permeability: The ability of a rock or unconsolidated material to transmit a fluid.

petrology: A general term for all the available methods to study the natural history of rocks.

physical property: Any property of a mineral that can be determined with the senses.

physical weathering: Any process whereby rocks are physically reduced in size.

piedmont glacier: An alpine glacier that has advanced beyond the base of a mountain onto the adjacent valley floor.

pillow lava: Basaltic lava that has cooled and solidified underwater.

planet: The celestial body that forms from a protoplanet by the melting and density separation of the mass into layers surrounding a dense core.

planetesimal: Small bodies orbiting around the Sun that coalesced to form the protoplanets, from which the planets evolved.

plastic flow: Flowage within a solid body.

plastic strain: The response to stress whereby a material consumes the applied energy and deforms permanently.

plate: The pieces of the lithosphere involved in plate tectonics.

playa lake: A shallow lake found in arid regions that holds water during the wet season but disappears during the dry season.

Plinean phase: A violent phase of volcanic eruption in which pyroclastic material is blown tens of thousands of feet into the air.

plunge: The angle between the fold axis and the horizontal; the process by which folds come to an end.

porosity: The percentage of a rock or unconsolidated material represented by void space.

pressure melting: The melting of a solid due to the favoring of the liquid phase over the solid phase under pressure.

pressure surface: The surface associated with a confined aquifer to which water will rise when released from the aquifer.

primeval atom: The small sphere proposed by Georges Lemaître to contain all the matter in the Universe before the Big Bang.

proton: The subatomic particle in the nucleus of an atom with a single positive charge and a mass of 1 amu; it consists of two up quarks and one down quark (uud).

proton-proton chain: The reaction within a star whereby four hydrogen nuclei combine to create one helium nucleus.

protoplanet: In the planetesimal hypothesis, the intermediate stage between the planetesimal and a planet.

pyrite: A mineral with the composition FeS_2. Commonly called "fool's gold."

quark: A fundamental particle, of which there are six types; two of these, the up (u) quark and the down (d) quark, join to create protons and neutrons.

quarrying: The process of glacial erosion whereby rock fragments are loosened, detached, and removed from the bedrock.

radiolaria: Marine protozoans that secrete shells of silica.

Rayleigh wave: The surface seismic wave that is a combination of the compression wave motion and the vertical component of the shear motion.

recessional moraine: An accumulation of till deposited along the front edge of a glacier during a significantly long standstill in the retreat of the glacier.

recharge area: The site or area where water enters an aquifer system.

recumbent fold: A fold where the limbs approach the horizontal.

red giant star: A star that has finished its core hydrogen-burning stage and has begun hydrogen shell burning, resulting in the cooling and expansion of its outer layers.

regional water table: The water table underlying a region.

regolith: The accumulated solid products of weathering above bedrock.

rejuvenation: The process of renewed erosion by a stream in response to an increase in the distance between the stream channel and the base level.

relief: The average distance between the hilltops and valley floors in a region.

renewable resource: A material that, once harvested, will be replaced by a new unit within a reasonably short period of time, taken to be an average human lifetime.

Richter scale: The scale created by Charles Richter in 1934 that evaluates the actual earth movement and amount of energy released during an earthquake.

rift valley: A valley created by the rifting of a continent along a developing divergent plate margin.

rift zone: The zone of fractures that appears on land as the first sign of the development of a divergent plate margin.

right-lateral strike-slip fault: A strike-slip fault where an observer standing on one block would be required to turn to the right to find the same index locality on the other side of the fault.

Ring of Fire: The arc of volcanism along the eastern, northern, and western margins of the Pacific Ocean basin.

ripple marks: A series of parallel or sub-parallel, small-scale ridges and valleys that form as currents of wind or water move across the surface of a sand deposit.

rock fall: The free-fall mass-wasting process whereby a newly detached rock fragment falls from a steep slope.

rock fragments: Fragments of rock created by physical weathering.

rock transport: The lateral movement of masses of rock in response to the forces involved in the formation of foldbelt mountains.

rotational compression: Compression in which the forces act toward but not opposite to each other.

sabkha: A hot, dry desert environment within which significant thicknesses of salts accumulate by the evaporation of water. Usually a broad, nearly horizontal surface located along an ocean margin where water is introduced by the tides.

sandstone: A sedimentary rock consisting primarily of sand-sized particles.

sanitary landfill: A site where municipal waste is deposited, compacted, and buried in such a fashion to minimize potential environmental contamination.

sedimentary quartzite: A sandstone consisting nearly entirely of quartz grains cemented with silica.

sedimentary rock: A rock formed from the products of weathering.

Seismic Sea Wave Warning System: The system installed around the Pacific Ocean basin to warn low-lying areas of impending tsunamis.

seismic wave: A shock wave associated with an earthquake.

seismogram: The record from a seismograph.

seismograph: An instrument that detects an earthquake and provides a record of the generated seismic waves.

seismometer: An instrument that detects an earthquake but does not provide a record.

septic system: A system for the disposal of domestic sewage in lieu of a municipal disposal system.

shale: A fine-grained, thinly laminated sedimentary rock consisting primarily of clay minerals. The most abundant of all sedimentary rocks.

shallow-focus earthquake: An earthquake that occurs from the surface to depths of about 40 miles.

shear joint: A fracture generated by shear forces along which there has been no or little movement.

shear wave: A shock wave in which the material transmitting the wave moves perpendicular to the direction of propagation.

sheet silicate structure: The silicate structure in which the silicon tetrahedra are joined into sheets that are stacked one over the other and joined together by cations.

shield: That portion of the continental crust that has been relatively stable over a long period of time.

shield volcano: The type of volcano that forms by repeated flows of basaltic lava. Commonly, shield volcanoes form in association with oceanic hot spots, although some do form on land.

silicate anion: The major building block of the silicate minerals, consisting of four oxygen atoms and a single silicon atom with an overall −4 charge, $(SiO_4)^{4-}$.

silicate mineral: A mineral whose major component is the silicate anion.

silicon tetrahedron: The three-dimensional arrangement of the silicate anion.

single-chain silicate structure: The silicate structure consisting of parallel single chains of silicon tetrahedra joined together by cations.

singularity: The theoretical dimensionless point consisting totally of energy that preceded the Big Bang.

slickenside: A polished, smoothly striated surface resulting from the mutual abrasion of rocks on opposite sides of a fault.

slides: A group of mass-wasting processes intermediate between flows, which require significant amounts of water, and falls, which require the least amount of water.

solar mass: The mass of the Sun.

solar wind: The stream of charged subatomic particles flowing outward from the Sun.

solution sinkhole: The type of sinkhole that forms by the dissolution of rock at the intersection of shear joints.

SONAR: The echo-sounding device used to determine water depth.

sorting: The process whereby particles are separated by size.

specific gravity: The ratio of the weight of an object to the weight of an equal volume of water.

speleothem: Any formation of travertine, commonly called dripstone, that forms within a limestone cave or cavern.

spodosol: The humid, temperate-climate soil order that forms under conifer cover.

Stay Force: In the context of this discussion, the force that resists the downslope movement of loose materials.

stony-iron meteorite: The rarest of all meteorites.

stony meteorite: The most abundant of all meteorites, making up 93% of all meteorite falls.

strain: The response to stress.

stratification: A structure produced by the deposition of sediments in tabular units, such as beds or layers.

strato-volcano: The type of volcano associated with zones of subduction, consisting of alternating layers of pyroclastic material and andesitic lavas.

streak: The color of a powdered mineral.

stream volume: The cross-sectional area of a stream channel measured at the surface of the water.

strength: The ability to withstand stress without strain.

stress: Any applied force.

strike: The direction of the line of intersection of a plane with the horizontal.

strike-slip fault: A type of fault in which there is horizontal offset along a vertical fault plane with little or no vertical offset.

Strombolian phase: The phase of volcanic activity characterized by frequent explosive eruptions.

subduction: The process whereby one lithospheric plate moves beneath another.

supernova: A violent stellar explosion.

surface wave: The seismic waves that move out in all directions from the epicenter of an earthquake, consisting of Love and Rayleigh waves.

suspended load: The fine-grained portion of the stream load, primarily silt- and clay-sized, that is transported for considerable periods of time within the mass of water.

suture zone: The zone where continents weld together following a continent-continent collision.

symmetrical fold: A fold where the limbs dip away from the axial plane in opposite directions at the same angle of dip.

syncline: A concave upward fold in which the youngest rocks are in the core of the fold.

Taconic orogeny: A major orogenic event that affected the northern Appalachian region during Ordovician time.

temporary base level: Any base level, other than sea level, that can serve as a base level for a limited period of time.

tension: The type of stress in which the forces act directly away from each other.

tension joint: A fracture within a rock that has formed under tensional forces, along which there has been little or no movement.

terminal moraine: The deposit of till that marks the furthest extent of a glacier's advance.

Terrestrial Planets: The innermost four planets of the solar system.

texture: The general appearance of a rock in terms of the size, shape, and arrangements of the constituents.

thrust fault: A fault where the hanging wall has moved up relative to the footwall, and the angle between the fault plane and the horizontal is 45° or less.

transform fault: A special type of strike-slip movement that develops perpendicular to the trend of the oceanic ridge and allows the plates to move on a spherical surface.

triple alpha reaction: The nuclear reaction in which three helium nuclei combine to form a carbon nucleus.

tsunami: A sea wave of enormous energy generated by a submarine earthquake or volcanic eruption.

tuff: A general term for any rock composed of pyroclastic material.

turbulent flow: The type of fluid flow that involves both horizontal and vertical movement of the fluid.

ultimate base level: The level below which a stream cannot carve its channel. For exterior streams, the ultimate base level is sea level. For interior streams, it is the elevation of the basin in which the stream terminates.

ultisol: The humid, temperate-climate soil order that develops under hardwood forest cover.

unconfined aquifer: The type of aquifer associated with regional or perched watertables.

unloading: The process by which fractures form in rocks parallel to the surface as a result of the removal of the overlying rock by erosion.

U-shaped valley: The diagnostic cross-sectional shape of a valley carved by a glacier.

valley flat: The bedrock surface carved by a meandering stream.

valley train: The stratified, well-sorted material deposited by meltwater streams down-valley from the terminus of an alpine glacier.

van der Waals bonding: A weak intermolecular attractive force; the weakest of all chemical bonds.

ventifact: Any object carved by windblown sand.

viscosity: A property of all liquids; the resistance to flow.

Volcanian phase: The phase of volcanic eruption defined as infrequent but severe explosions.

V-shaped valley: The characteristic cross-section of a stream in Davis's state of youth.

water table: The contact between the zone of aeration and the zone of saturation.

weathering: Any process whereby rocks either disintegrate or decompose.

welded tuff: A tuff formed by pyroclastic materials that were partially molten at the time of deposition.

wet-based glacier: Glaciers in which a layer of water generated by pressure melting separates the ice from the underlying bedrock. Most alpine glaciers are wet-based.

white dwarf star: The compact remnant of a low-massed star, in which the core is becoming dominated by helium.

Wilson cycle: A theory proposing that plate tectonics represents a cyclic process in which a supercontinent breaks up, forming new continents, that then move away from each other for about 250 million years; at that point, they change direction and return to form another supercontinent 250 million years later.

x-ray diffraction: An instrumental analytical technique that allows the identification of solid crystalline materials.

yellow boy: The deposit of limonite, FeO(OH), that accompanies the contamination of streams by acid mine drainage.

youth: The initial stage in Davis's theory of landscape evolution, in which the distance between the stream channels and their base levels is at a maximum.

zone of aeration: The zone above the water table, within which the pores are devoid of water except during times of precipitation.

zone of saturation: The zone below the water table, within which the pores are filled with water down to the deepest penetration of groundwater.

zone of subduction: The zone where the oceanic lithospheric plate is being driven beneath the overlying continental plate.

Biographical Notes

M. K. Hubbert (1903–1989). Hubbert was born in San Saba, TX, in 1903. He attended Weatherford Junior College from 1921 to 1923 and received his B.S. and M.S. from the University of Chicago. He taught geophysics at Columbia University and received a Ph.D. in 1937. During World War II, he was a senior analyst at the Board of Economic Warfare in Washington, DC. Following the war, he joined Shell Oil Company, where he was director of the research laboratory. He retired from Shell Oil in 1964 and joined the U.S. Geological Survey, where he was a senior geophysicist. Hubbert was best known for his studies of petroleum and for his predictions of the peaks of domestic and world production, both of which have been proven to be quite accurate.

James Hutton (1726–1797). Hutton was born in Edinburgh, Scotland, and educated at the University of Edinburgh, where he studied medicine for three years. He completed his medical studies in Paris and received his doctorate in medicine at Leiden in 1749. With no medical positions available, he abandoned medicine and devoted himself to the study of agriculture on a plot of land that he inherited from his father. He traveled widely to learn the practical aspects of farming. It was during these journeys that he began to study Earth's surface and surface processes. In 1785, he published a paper entitled "Theory of the Earth, or an Investigation of the Laws Observable in the Composition, Dissolution and Restoration of Land upon the Globe." In this paper, which he presented to the newly established Royal Society of Edinburgh, he expressed views that were totally alien to most of the earth scientists of the day. He stated that the rocks seen at Earth's surface were formed from the wastes of older rocks that were carried by streams to the ocean, where they were deposited on the ocean bottom and converted to new rocks by great pressures. These rocks were then uplifted to Earth's surface where, upon exposure to the atmosphere, they began to decay to form the wastes of which future rocks would be made. During the later part of his life, he devoted his time to writing a text entitled *Theory of the Earth*, which was published in two volumes in 1795. It was largely Hutton's views in this publication that built the foundation for the modern science of geology.

J. Tuzo Wilson (1908–1993). The son of a Scottish engineer, Wilson graduated with degrees in geology and geophysics from the University of Toronto (B.A. and Sc.D.) and Princeton University (Ph.D.). During the late 1930s, he worked for the Geological Survey of Canada, where he became one of the first geologists to use aerial photography to study Earth's surface. As a result of these photographic surveys, Wilson and five colleagues were able to prepare the first tectonic map of Canada. Following his service with the Canadian Army Engineers during World War II, Wilson was appointed professor of geophysics at the University of Toronto. During his 20-year tenure, he made significant contributions that eventually led to the formulation of the theory of plate tectonics. Wilson was first to explain the formation of hot spot volcanoes associated with mantle plumes, the existence of transform faults, the opening and closing of the ocean basins, and the concept now known as the Wilson cycle, which proposes the cyclic creation, breaking up, and reformation of supercontinents.

Alfred Wegener (1880–1930). Wegener earned a Ph.D. in astronomy from the University of Berlin in 1904. Following graduation, his interests centered on geophysics, meteorology, and climatology. During this time, he championed the use of balloons to track air currents. Following an expedition to Greenland to study the circulation of Arctic air masses, he accepted a position of tutor at the University of Marburg. While at Marburg, Wegener came across a paper describing the identical assemblages of plant and animal fossils on opposite sides of the Atlantic. He also noticed what many other observers of maps had seen, namely, the distinct similarity of the Atlantic coastal outlines of South America and Africa, an observation that no doubt planted the seeds of continental drift in Wegener's mind. Wegener was drafted into the German army in 1914. After being wounded in battle, he was released from combat duty and served out the remainder of the war in the army weather-forecasting service. Following his military service, Wegener continued to collect evidence to demonstrate that South America and Africa were once joined into a larger continent. In 1915, he published the first edition of *The Origin of Continents and Oceans*, in which he outlined his theory of continental drift. Reaction to his ideas was almost universally hostile, certainly among the Northern Hemisphere geologists who dominated the science of geology at the time. Only geologists living in the Southern Hemisphere were attracted to his theory. It would be more than a half century before he would be shown to be essentially correct in most aspects of his theory of a supercontinent that broke up to create the modern continental masses. Unfortunately, the theory of plate tectonics would come long after his death.

Bibliography

Benn, D., and D. Evans. *Glaciers and Glaciation*. London: Hodder Arnold, 1998. An excellent treatment of the formation and structure of glaciers and their influence on landscapes.

Bland, W., and D. Rolls. *Weathering: An Introduction to the Scientific Principles*. New York: Arnold, 1998. A basic text dealing with principles of bonding and structure as related to the silicate and non-silicate minerals; the bulk properties of rocks; and the scientific principles behind physical, chemical, and biological weathering, including rates and intensities.

Bloom, A. L. *Geomorphology: A Systematic Analysis of Late Cenozoic Landforms*. Upper Saddle River, NJ: Prentice-Hall, 1998. Deals in detail with the late Cenozoic evolution of the present-day landscape in the context of the changing positions of the continents and the subsequent climatic changes from a globally warm "greenhouse" climate to the current interglacial interval within the "ice house" of the Quaternary period.

Bryant, E. *Tsunami: The Underrated Hazard*. Cambridge: Cambridge University Press, 2001. A comprehensive discussion of the nature and processes of tsunami formation, including field evidence for the detection of past tsunami events. Describes particular events linked to earthquakes, volcanic eruptions, submarine landslides, and meteorite impacts.

Costa, J. E., and V. R. Baker. *Surficial Geology*. New York: Wiley, 1981. An excellent upper-division undergraduate or graduate-level treatment of the processes that shape the land surface.

Cox, A., and F. J. Vine. *Plate Tectonics: How It Works*. Palo Alto, CA: Blackwell, 1986. This book is for anyone whose imagination has been captured by popular accounts of plate tectonics and would like to know more.

Crozier, M. J. *Landslides: Causes, Consequences, and Environment*. Dover, NH: Croom Helm, 1986. This text deals with the causes of slope instability, the mechanics of slopes, and site investigations to assess slope stability, and potential remedial procedures that may be called on to increase slope stability.

Davis, G. H., and S. J. Reynolds. *Structural Geology of Rocks and Regions*, 2nd ed. New York: Wiley, 1996. An advanced treatment of kinematic and dynamic analyses, deformational mechanisms, and microstructures, as well as the basic geologic structures of folds, faults, joints, cleavage, lineations, shear zones, and progressive deformation related to plate tectonics.

De Boer, J. Z., and D. T. Sanders. *Volcanoes in Human History: The Far-Reaching Effects of Major Eruptions*. Princeton: Princeton University Press, 2001. Discusses examples of major volcanic eruptions and their worldwide effects, including eruptions in the Hawaiian Islands, the eruption of Thera and the possible effect on the Minoan civilization, the eruption of Vesuvius in A.D. 79, the 1815 eruption of Tamboro and the "year without a summer," and the death and destruction brought on by the 1883 eruption of Krakatoa.

Decker, R. W., and B. B. Decker. *Volcanoes*. New York: W. H. Freeman, 1997. Robert Decker was the scientist-in-charge at the Hawaiian Volcano Observatory and, in this book, has documented a lifetime of study in an excellent treatment of the basics of volcanism.

Deer, W. A., J. Zussman, and R. A. Howie. *An Introduction to the Rock-Forming Minerals*, 2nd ed. Boston: Addison-Wesley, 1996. An excellent reference book for the serious student of mineralogy.

Easterbrook, D. J. *Surface Processes and Landforms*. Upper Saddle River, NJ: Prentice-Hall, 1999. A textbook devoted to the interrelationship between surface processes and the subsequent kinds of evolved landscapes.

Edwards, John D. "Crude Oil and Alternate Energy Production Forecasts for the Twenty-First Century: The End of the Hydrocarbon Era." *AAPG Bulletin*, August 1997, vol. 81/9, pp. 1292–1305. Crude oil will be able to supply increasing demand until peak world production is reached. Conventional crude oil production in the United States is forecast to terminate about 2090, and world production will be close to exhaustion by 2100.

Harris, A. G., E. Tuttle, and S. D. Tuttle, *Geology of National Parks*, 5th ed. Dubuque, IA: Kendall/Hunt Publishing, 1997. This book presents a complete geologic description of each of our national parks, from the geologic origin of the rocks and rock structures to the physical features. *Geology of National Parks* and *Parks and Plates* (see Lille, below) are two books that should be in the library of anyone who wants to fully understand, appreciate, and enjoy visits to our national parks.

Hawking, S. *A Brief History of Time*. New York: Bantam, 1988. Hawking explains the intricacies of the Universe, from the Big Bang to black holes, to the non-specialist reader, without resorting to mathematical complexities.

Hibbard, J. J. *Mineralogy: A Geologist's Point of View*. New York: McGraw-Hill, 2001. Practical insights into the formation of minerals and their physical properties, crystallography, and place in the geologic environment.

Hough, S. E. *Earthquake Science: What We Know (and Don't Know) about Earthquakes*. Princeton: Princeton University Press, 2002. In jargon-free presentations, Hough discusses advances in earthquake detection and Earth movements and addresses as-yet-unsolved problems, such as earthquake prediction, hazard assessment, and other issues at the forefront of modern seismology.

Ingebritsen, S.E. *Groundwater in Geologic Processes*. Cambridge: Cambridge University Press, 2006. The book is written at the upper-division undergraduate or graduate level. The style of the text is lucid and concise and includes discussions of the involvement of groundwater in geologic processes such as rock deformation, sediment compaction, diagenesis, metamorphism, and sub-sea hydrology.

Lille, R. J. *Parks and Plates*. New York, London: W. W. Norton & Co., 2005. Following an introduction to the basic principles of plate tectonics, this book beautifully illustrates how plate tectonics has created what one sees in many of our national parks. A must-read for those preparing visits to any of the national parks whose structures are specifically determined by plate movements.

Moores, E. M. *Shaping of the Earth: Tectonics of Continents and Oceans: Readings from Scientific American Magazine*. New York: Freeman, 1990. A compilation of articles that comprehensively cover the topic of plate tectonics for the non-scientist but informed reader.

Ollier, C., and C. Pain. *Regolith, Soils, and Landforms*. New York: Freeman, 1996. Describes many aspects of the regolith, including formation, weathering zones, how the regolith may affect human health, the formation and destruction of regolith materials, and concepts involved in landscape evolution.

Price, M. *Introducing Groundwater*. London: Routledge, 2004. Basic information is presented in a style intended for the non-specialist reader, with technical terms and mathematics kept to a minimum.

The text covers current problems such as pollution, droughts, and long-term water shortages.

Prothero, D. R., and F. L. Schwab. *Sedimentary Geology*. New York: Freeman, 1998. This is basically an introductory textbook for geology majors covering sedimentary rocks and stratigraphy. Also includes current research in tectonics and sedimentation, focusing on critical geologic principles.

Renton, John J. *Planet Earth*. Dubuque, IA: Kendall-Hunt Publishing Co., 2002. A basic textbook written primarily for the introductory geology student that covers all the major aspects of physical geology.

Rifkin, J. *The Hydrogen Economy*. New York: Tarcher/Putnam, 2002. Rifkin observes that we are fast approaching the watershed for fossil fuels, in particular oil, with dire consequences for industrial civilization. He points out that hydrogen is the most abundant element in the Universe and, if properly harnessed, will be the ultimate fuel of the future.

Silk, J. *A Brief History of the Universe*. New York: Freeman, 1994. An in-depth discussion of cosmology, including standard cosmology, particle cosmology, and quantum cosmology.

Thomas, L. *Coal Geology*. New York: Wiley, 2002. The text covers the physical and chemical properties of coal, coal petrology, age and occurrences of coal, coal exploration, and mining technology and successfully bridges the gap between the academic and practical aspects of coal geology.

Twiss, R. J., and E. M. Moores. *Structural Geology*. New York: Freeman, 1992. A comprehensive text and reference book for advanced undergraduate and graduate-level courses.

Winter, J. D. *Introduction to Igneous and Metamorphic Petrology*. Upper Saddle River, NJ: Prentice-Hall, 2001. An introduction to the main concepts of igneous and metamorphic rocks, with their relationship relative to plate tectonics and orogenic activity.

Website:

www.groundwater.org Groundwater is a major source of water and will be increasingly important in years to come. This website of The Groundwater Foundation provides a wide variety of topics for anyone wishing to expand their understanding of groundwater.